SOILS MANUAL

for

Design of Asphalt Pavement Structures

THE ASPHALT INSTITUTE

SECOND EDITION

Second Printing

April 1963

May 1964

Manual Series No. 10 (MS-10)

Soil. Sediments or other unconsolidated accumulations of solid particles produced by the physical and chemical disintegration of rocks, and which may or may not contain organic matter.

Soil-Aggregate (Dense-Graded Aggregate). Natural or prepared mixtures consisting predominantly of stone, gravel, or sand and containing silt-clay (minus No. 200 material).

AASHO Designation: M 146

FOREWORD

With the publication of this *Soils Manual*, The Asphalt Institute has moved further toward rounding out a complete shelf of engineering manuals dealing with the design and construction of asphalt pavement structures. Others in the series include those on *Thickness Design* (of Asphalt Pavement Structures), *Mix Design Methods* (for Hot-Mix Asphalt Paving), the *Asphalt Plant Manual*, and the *Asphalt Paving Manual*. (A full list of Asphalt Institute technical publications may be found at the back of this book.)

It is a basic engineering dictum that all asphalt paving design procedures must start with a fundamental consideration of the underlying soil conditions. The properties and characteristics of the foundation soils will determine to a critical degree the thickness of the pavement structure which it will support. Consequently, this publication may properly be regarded as a primary text, from which all pavement design and construction procedures flow.

In preparing this manual, The Asphalt Institute has borrowed freely from the published methods and procedures recommended by the American Association of State Highway Officials, the American Society for Testing and Materials, and the U. S. Army Corps of Engineers. To these professional agencies The Asphalt Institute wishes to acknowledge its debt and to express its appreciation. To those state highway departments and individuals who have made valuable contributions, the Institute also is grateful.

Like all engineering manuals of its kind, this *Soils Manual* is considered tentative in its initial publication form. Inevitably, typographic and literary "bugs" will turn up, and minor errors in the text may have to be ironed out in subsequent printings. Our readers are cordially invited to call our attention to any questionable passages. Nevertheless, every effort has been made to assure completeness and accuracy in this publication and the Institute trusts the manual will prove a valuable reference aid to the highway engineer.

THE ASPHALT INSTITUTE

ASPHALT INSTITUTE BUILDING

COLLEGE PARK, MARYLAND

APRIL 1963

Printed in the U.S.A.

CONTENTS

TABLES AND FIGURES

Part I

Page

Part II

Appendices

PART I

General Classification of Soils

Chapter I

INTRODUCTION

1.01 GENERAL

The use of asphalt pavement structures for streets, highways, airports and other purposes has increased quite rapidly during the last two decades. To meet this urgent demand for asphalt pavement structures, engineers have worked assiduously to develop a method for properly designing these structures. The urgency of the situation in many cases and differences in climate, soils, traffic type, and density combined with a lack of proper communication between engineers, at times, has led to the development of several methods of asphalt pavement design. The popularity of asphalt pavement structures in many countries having varied climates and changing traffic requirements is a tribute to these design methods, asphalt materials, and the engineering profession.

A single universal and rational method for the structural design of asphalt pavements is the goal of asphalt paving technologists. In the meantime, engineers charged with the design of asphalt pavements will usually have a choice of design methods.

Most design methods now in use have been described in engineering literature. As a service to engineers, The Asphalt Institute has authorized a series of manuals that discuss the design of asphalt pavement structures. These manuals are: (1) *Thickness Design—Asphalt Pavement Structures for Streets and Highways*, (2) *Asphalt Pavements for Airports*, and (3) *Mix Design Methods for Asphalt Concrete and other Hot Mix Types*. The first two manuals outline procedures for several pavement design methods in current use. The third manual differs from the others in that it describes in detail the laboratory test procedures employed by the most widely used methods for hot-mix design.

1.02 PURPOSE AND SCOPE

Numerous requests have been received by the Institute for detailed laboratory and field soil test procedures used for obtaining design information required by the methods in the first two manuals listed above. It became apparent, therefore, that these manuals should be supplemented by another which would give detailed field and laboratory soil test procedures for determining the design values for the various methods. Although these procedures are described separately in numerous technical journals, they are not readily available to the average engineer and technician. Little effort has been made in the past to collect and publish these test procedures in a single volume which would be a convenient reference for those needing this information. The Institute has prepared this manual for that purpose.

Origin, composition, and properties of soil, and significance of tests for soil materials, are discussed briefly as refresher information. The soil survey is presented in some detail because of its importance in obtaining accurate test results.

The three soil classification systems in common use and the three principal testing methods used in selecting pavement thickness are included in this manual. These are as follows: (1) American Association of State Highway Officials (AASHO) Classification for Soils, (2) Unified Soil Classification System, (3) Federal Aviation Agency Method of Soil and Subgrade Classification, (4) California Bearing Ratio Method, (5) Bearing Value Determination-Plate Bearing Test, and (6) Hveem's Resistance Value (R) Method. It is not intended that the classification systems be used for final thickness design but as preliminary tools leading to the final design.

Although some editing of test procedures has been undertaken for consistency of style, they are essentially the procedures described in the most recent literature by individuals or organizations who developed and use them. In most instances the references from which the procedures were obtained are cited in each chapter.

It should be recognized that current methods for evaluating soils and aggregates used in asphalt pavement structures are generally considered to be of an empirical nature. Engineering judgment, therefore, must be used in applying the results of these tests.

The general nature and status of soil testing is well described in the introductory section of "Procedures for Testing Soils," American Society for Testing Materials, April, 1958. The following quotations on the general subject of soil testing illustrate the viewpoint of experts:

". . . The very fact of having test methods for the study of soil properties may suggest to the unwary that soils are similar to other materials of construction, and therefore always susceptible to routine testing in the laboratory. That this is not the case, all who have gained any experience in the use of soil mechanics know well. The necessity for the vital use of judgment in all phases of soil testing should never be forgotten . . ."

". . . Something more fundamental is needed, however, than merely the correct recording and standardizing of methods for soil testing. This is well known to all who are experienced in the practice of soil mechanics, since they come to know instinctively that all soil test results *must* be assessed and applied only in the light of all the factors relating to the site from which the soil sample was obtained, the way in which the sample has been handled, the way in which the testing was carried out and by whom—in other words, with judgment . . ."

". . . Soil engineers should realize that they are dealing with an inherently variable, complex, and in many respects an unusual kind of engineering material in their work with soils. In marked contrast to the essential uniformity of the common structural materials, the predictability of their behavior within the range of common working stresses, and the marked constancy of their responses and properties for all common usages unaffected by external environmental influences, soils should not be expected to follow such simple patterns of behavior . . ."

Thus, it is apparent that in using the basic test methods outlined in this manual, the engineer must give proper consideration to climate, traffic, and other factors which are an inherent part of the specific design problem, adjusting these basic methods as required.

The number of evaluation methods described in this manual was purposely limited to those referred to in other Asphalt Institute manuals. Those described in the chapters that follow are the methods most widely accepted today. The importance and use of aerial photographs for highway location, drainage, soil studies, and design are also discussed briefly in Chapter III.

Several routine soil tests are required by more than one of the design methods described in Chapters VIII through X. Although procedures for these tests are generally well known and described in engineering literature, the AASHO procedures for each have been included in the Appendix to this manual. This was done to help make this manual a one-volume reference for pavement design soil test procedures.

Chapter II

2.01 DEFINITION AND ORIGIN OF SOIL

The word *soil* has numerous meanings and connotations to different groups of professional people who deal with this material. To most soil engineers it is any earthen material, excluding bed rock. Soil is composed of loosely bound mineral grains of various sizes and shapes, organic material, water and gases.

The bonds holding solid particles together in most soils are relatively weak in comparison to most sound rocks. In fact an air-dried sample of soil will crumble and break down within a relatively short period when placed in water and gently agitated.

The solid particles of which soils are composed are usually the products of both physical and chemical action (weathering). Deposits of these weathered solid constituents may be found near or directly above the bed rock (residual soils) or organic deposits (cumulose soils) from which they were formed (see Figure II-1). Many soil deposits, however, have been transported from their point of origin to new locations by such agents as water, wind, ice, or volcanic action. Water-transported soils are classed as alluvial (deposited by moving water on flood plains, deltas, and bars), marine (deposited in salt water) and lacustrine (deposited in fresh water lakes). Ice-transported soils are generally called drift or glacial till. Soils transported by wind may be referred to as aeolian soils.

2.02 SOIL TEXTURE

The size and distribution of mineral grains present in a given soil depend upon many factors, including min-

— 5 —

eralogical composition, climate, length of weathering period and method of transportation. The texture, or sizes of particles present in a given soil, frequently plays an important role in classifying the soil and influencing its engineering properties. In general, soil texture has been used to divide earthen materials into two broad categories, coarse-grained and fine soils (Figure II-2).

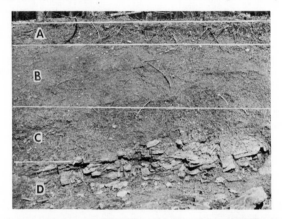

Figure II-1—Residual Soil Profile (above) from Fairfax Co., Va., Showing Four Horizons, and Example (below) of Soil Profile With Well-Defined Horizons—*Courtesy, Virginia Dept. of Highways*

Figure II-2—Soil Texture, Showing Coarse-Grained and Fine-Grained Soils

Coarse-grained soils have been further subdivided into boulder, gravel, or sand fractions, depending on grain size. Moreover, the engineering properties of the coarse-grained group often are strongly influenced by texture and gradation.

Fine-grained soils have been divided into silts and clays. The soil grains of which silts and clays are composed are so small that they cannot be distingiushed with the unaided eye. Moreover, their engineering properties are more strongly influenced by surface and electrical forces than by gravity forces as is true in the case of the coarse-grained fractions. Therefore, texture plays a less important role in determining the engineering properties of this group than for the coarse-grained group. Silts are normally less plastic than clays and have little or no dry strength.

2.03 SOIL STRUCTURE

The manner in which the individual particles in a soil mass are arranged has been referred to as *primary structure*. For the coarse-grained soils, primary structure can frequently be observed with the unaided eye or a hand lens. Methods for observing the structure of fine-grained soils (silts and clays) have been slower in developing. Recently developed techniques in the field of electron microscopy, however, promise to become helpful in observing the structure of these soils.

Although primary structure cannot be observed in many instances and although it probably varies considerably in what otherwise may appear to be a homogeneous deposit, engineers have attempted to postulate and classify various primary soil structures. Some of these are: (a) single grained, (b) honeycomb, (c) flocculent (Figure II-3).

Soils frequently exhibit another type of structure which has been called *secondary structure*. This term refers to systems of cracks, fissures, and other discontinuities which sometimes develop subsequent to a soil's formation or deposition.

A. SINGLE-GRAINED

B. HONEYCOMB

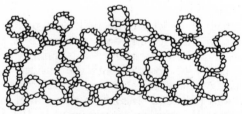

C. FLOCCULENT

Figure II-3—Three Types of Soil Structure

Both primary and secondary structure often play an important role in determining such soil engineering properties as permeability, elasticity, compressibility, and shear strength.

2.04 WATER, SOLIDS, AND AIR RELATIONSHIPS

Ordinarily, the only way to detect the presence of an unusual secondary soil structure in a deposit is by visual examination. In the case of primary structures, however, visual observations usually are insufficient, and indirect means are employed to evaluate this factor roughly. To do this it has been found convenient to think of any soil as being composed of three states of matter—solid, water, and gas or air. Although it is impossible to make this separation into three separate states in the laboratory, it is convenient to represent soil as shown in Figure II-4 below.

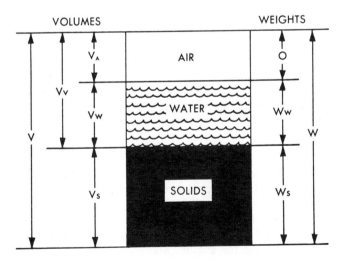

Figure II-4—Schematic Diagram Showing Three Phases of a Soil

Figure II-4 is a schematic or block diagram for a three-phase soil, or a soil in which all three states of matter are present. Under some conditions, such as oven drying and complete saturation, only two phases or states of matter will be present and represented in one of these diagrams. Gravimetric or weight terms are shown on the right side of this diagram and volumetric terms on the left. Suitable subscripts (a, w, s, and v) are used to denote air, water, solid, and void respectively.

The ratio of certain weight and volume terms shown in Figure II-4 have been defined and are employed in soil engineering not only to obtain an indirect measure of soil structure but to estimate settlement, permeability, and state of compaction. Some of these ratios, or proportions, and defined symbolically as follows:

(a) water content $w = \dfrac{W_w}{W_s} \times 100$,

(b) void ratio $e = \dfrac{V_v}{V_s}$

and (c) porosity $n = \dfrac{V_v}{V} \times 100$.

In many instances numerical values for these and other defined ratios may be obtained for a given soil by making sufficient weight and volume measurements on a representative sample of the material.

2.05 ENGINEERING PROPERTIES OF SOIL

Such factors as parent material, mineralogical composition, organic matter content, climate, age, method of transportation, place of deposition, method and degree of compaction, soil texture, soil gradation, and soil structure, though often interrelated, all play important roles in determining the engineering properties of soils.

Some more important engineering soil properties are: (a) permeability, (b) elasticity, (c) plasticity, (d) cohesion, (e) shearing strength, (f) compressibility, (g) shrinkage and swell and (h) frost susceptibility.

To the civil engineer permeability usually means the ease or difficulty with which water will flow or pass through the pores of a soil. Soil texture, gradation, degree of compaction, and primary structure strongly influence a given soil's relative permeability. Coarse-grained soils usually are much more permeable than fine-grained soils, although the presence of small quantities of fines or cementing materials in coarse-grained soils and cracks, fissures, and holes in fine-grained soils sometimes alter this pattern. Fairly reliable laboratory and field tests have been devised for determining the permeability of coarser-grained soils.

Elasticity refers to the ability of a soil to return to its original shape after having been deformed by a load for a short period of time. This elastic deformation or re-bound deflection which accompanies the application of a light load results from the elastic deformation of individual mineral particles and in some instances the elastic deformation of the "sponge rubber-like" structure of the soil mass. In most soils and for most engineering applications, this deformation is quite small and often neglected. However, its importance in highway engineering is becoming more widely recognized.

Plasticity refers to the ability of a material to be deformed rapidly without cracking or crumbling and then maintain that deformed shape after the deforming force has been released. This non-reversible, or plastic, deformation is probably the sum of a large number of small slippages at grain-to-grain contact points and minute local structural collapses throughout the soil mass. Plastic deformation can become large and an important factor in highway and foundation engineering work.

It has been reasoned that as the plastic deformations in a soil become larger under the action of increasingly

Figure II-5—Three Types of Shear Failure—Courtesy, Virginia Council of Highway Investigation and Research

greater applied loads, a reorientation of soil particles begins to take place in certain critical zones within a soil mass. When the loads have become sufficiently large and a sufficient number of the soil particles in this critical zone are, perhaps, oriented parallel to one another, the soil mass begins to fail in shear within these critical zones. At or near this point the shearing resistance or strength of the soil is said to have been exceeded. Figure II-5 shows soil samples that have failed in shear.

The shearing strength of a soil is the result of friction between the particles, and cohesion. Cohesion of a soil is all of the shear strength not due to friction. Cohesion, and therefore shearing strength, is not constant but varies with changes in water content, rate and time of loading, confining pressure and numerous other factors. However, soils compacted dry of optimum moisture content usually exhibit greater shear strength than those compacted wet of optimum. The shearing strength of soils is a complex problem and much research is being done to find the best procedures for determining this property.

By definition materials which deform under the action of applied loads without changing volume have a Poisson's ratio equal to one-half. If, however, the deformation is entirely due to volume change, Poisson's ratio is equal to zero for that material. Reliable determinations of Poisson's ratio for soils are very difficult to obtain. Nevertheless, values of this ratio ranging between 0.0 and 0.5 are to be expected for most soils. This means that the deformation which accompanies the application of a load to a soil usually is composed of two parts, namely, elastic-plastic deformation and volume change.

Since the mineral grains and water in a soil mass are relatively incompressible, any volume change which occurs in the soil is, for the most part, due to a change in the soil structure accompanied by the expulsion of air or water, or both, from the soil mass. Compressibility as it is normally applied to soil refers to that portion of the volume change deformation resulting from the expulsion of only the pore water. Consolidation is another term which is used to describe this phenomenon. Compaction is a term which normally is employed to describe a process of densification in which the volume change is due almost entirely to the expulsion of air from the soil mass.

Compressibility, therefore, is influenced greatly by soil structure and the past stress history of the deposit. Deposits which develop as a result of a sedimentation process usually are more compressible than their residual or wind-blown counterparts. Laboratory methods for determining the relative compressibility of most soils have been devised and are widely used.

Frequently, volume change deformations occur in soil masses without any application or removal of external loads. This may be caused by at least two different phenomena. For example, the lowering of the ground water table in an area would, as a result, increase the soil stresses which are effective in producing a volume change within compressible layers below the original ground water level and lead to the settlement of fills or structures at or near the surface. In other instances the volume change deformations which occur in soils, independent of any externally applied load, may be the result of what is known as *shrinkage* or *swell phenomena.*

Shrinking and swelling are more pronounced in the fine grained soils, especially clays. Both shrinking and swelling result from a build-up and release of capillary tensile stresses within the soil's pore water and the varying degree of thirst for water which certain clay minerals have. Fortunately, most high volume change soils in the United States occur in belts or regions that are well known to most soil engineers. In most highway situations, the use of these high volume change soils should be avoided if possible. Where their use cannot be avoided, measures often are taken to reduce their capacity to swell, or to reduce fluctuations in their moisture content. Clays with high volume change capacity frequently have high liquid limits and plasticity

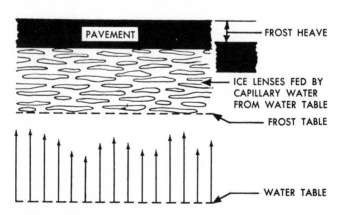

Figure II-6—Frost Heave is Caused by Ice Lenses Forming Beneath the Pavement Structure

indices. Laboratory tests are available to help identify and determine the swell of soils. (See Chapters VIII and X.)

The ice formed, as water in a pond freezes, thickens in a downward direction, being fed by water from below. Ice layers in frost-susceptible soils grow in the same way (Figure II-6). For ice layers or lenses to grow in a soil, three basic conditions must be present: (1) freezing temperatures in the soil, (2) a water table close enough to the frost line to feed the growing ice lenses, and (3) characteristics in the soil favorable to the rapid movement of capillary water upward from the water table. Where freezing temperatures are prolonged and the frost line penetrates deep into the soil, the ice layers that are formed cause the soil to heave at the surface, equivalent to the thicknesses of all the ice layers. The three most common methods for reducing the probability of detrimental frost heave in a frost-susceptible soil are the use of non-frost-susceptible subbases and bases, lowered water tables, and impermeable cutoff blankets between the subgrade and the subbase or base.

Chapter III

3.01 SOIL SURVEY

The soil survey is as important to the proper design of the pavement structure as the classification and strength tests. If the information recorded and the samples submitted to the laboratory are not representative, the results of the tests, no matter how precise, will be misleading and meaningless. The soil survey, therefore, must be made with accuracy.

The American Association of State Highway Officials Standard Method of Surveying and Sampling Soils for Highway Purposes (Designation T 86-54) is presented in the following paragraphs as a guide for conducting the soil survey. For additional information concerning soil surveys and the sampling of soils, The Asphalt Institute recommends "Procedures for Testing Soils" (published by the American Society for Testing Materials, April, 1958) and "Subsurface Exploration and Sampling of Soils for Civil Engineering Purposes" (by M. Juul Hvorslev, published by the American Society of Civil Engineers, November, 1949).

3.02 SURVEYING AND SAMPLING SOILS FOR HIGHWAY PURPOSES (AASHO DESIGNATION: T86-54).

Purpose of the Soil Survey

1. A soil survey is an essential part of a preliminary engineering survey for location and design purposes. Information on the distribution of soils and ground-water conditions must be obtained before a reasonable and economic design can be developed for a highway project.

A detailed soil survey provides pertinent information on the following subjects:

(a) The location of the road, both vertically and horizontally.

(b) The location and selection of borrow material for fills and subgrade treatment.

(c) The design and location of ditches, culverts, and drains.

(d) The design of the roadway section.

(e) The need for subgrade treatment and the type of treatment required.

(f) The location of local sources of construction materials for base and wearing courses.

(g) The selection of the type of surface and its design.

Scope of the Survey

2. The soil survey consists of the following parts:

(a) The study of all existing information on soil, and ground-water conditions occurring in the vicinity of the proposed road location.

(b) The exploration of the site of the road location by auger borings or other methods,[1] and the preparation of soil profiles showing the significant soil layers (horizons), the critical depths to bedrock, and water table; and the extent of adverse ground conditions such as swamps or peat bogs. In areas of proposed deep rock cuts geologic cross sections may be required in addition to the soil profile.

(c) The identification of the various soil types from soil profile characteristics occurring on the proposed road project.

(d) The taking of representative samples of soil and local construction materials for laboratory testing.

(e) The selection of undisturbed samples of soil for strength tests if required for the design of fills, cut slopes or bridge foundations.

(f) The study of pavement performance of roads constructed over

different soil conditions to develop general design recommendations.

Equipment

3. The amount and type of equipment required for making a survey depends upon the nature of the terrain and the use that will be made of the survey information. The following list of equipment should suffice for ordinary conditions. Additional equipment may be required to handle special conditions as they are encountered during the survey:

(a) Two 3-ft. soil augers (1½ inch, screw type), and ten 3-ft. extensions with couplings (Fig. A).

(b) Four 3-ft. post augers (4 inch) and ten 3-ft. extensions with couplings.

(c) One 3-ft. post auger (6 inch), constructed for use with post auger (4 inch) extensions.

(d) One sounding rod (⅜ inch, 6 ft. long with tempered spike and wedge ends).

(e) One peat sampler (see Fig. B).

(f) Two pipe wrenches (8-inch).

(g) One trench pick.

(h) One drain spade.

(i) A supply of sample bags and identification tags.

(j) A ball of twine.

(k) One engineer's level and level rod (12 ft., 3 sections).

(l) One 100-ft. metallic tape and one 6-ft. folding rule.

(m) One roll of 20-inch cross section paper (10 divisions to the inch each way).

(n) Notebooks and pencils.

(o) A supply of survey stakes.

(p) One axe and one 10-lb. sledge.

(q) One camera and supply of films.

(r) A supply of marking crayon.

(s) One canvas (6 by 6 ft.).

---

1 Test pits, churn or rotary drills, wash borings and geophysical methods are used in exploration of areas where rock or the presence of numerous boulders hinder auger boring operations.

(t) One 8-oz. bottle of dilute HCl for carbonate determinations.

Typical sampling equipment usually used for making highway soil surveys are shown in figures B and C.

Preliminary Study of Site Data

4. Prior to starting field work the literature should be reviewed to obtain general information useful in planning and organizing the survey work. Topographic maps, airphotos, geologic maps and county agricultural soil maps have been published for many sections of the country. A study of information of this type, when available for the area in which the survey is to be made, will justify the time required for the study. It is important that the engineer recognize the limitations of various types of maps. Some maps show considerable detail while others are of the reconnaissance type and show more generalized conditions.

Wherever county soil maps prepared by the Bureau of Plant Industry,[2] U. S. Department of Agriculture, are available, they should

---

2 Prior to October 16, 1938 these maps were prepared by the Bureau of Chemistry and Soils.

be studied. The limits of the various soil types and the soil profile characteristics of each soil type should be noted. A study of the descriptive text and an examination of similar soil areas in the field should enable the engineer to establish the range in soil profile characteristics for each soil type shown on the map. Each soil type has a distinctive soil profile and will have a characteristic range in parent material, relief, and vegetation. These criteria can be used to assist in the identification of the various soil types and thus enable the engineer to subdivide the terrain into various map units which reflect soil conditions likely to require similar engineering treatment.

A study of soil keys which show the interrelation of various map units with parent material, relief, and drainage conditions should assist the engineer in field identification of soils. This related information will be found useful in the interpretation of geologic or topographic maps or in the correlation of soil types with airphoto soil patterns in areas not covered by county soil maps.

In areas where there are no county soil maps and a limited

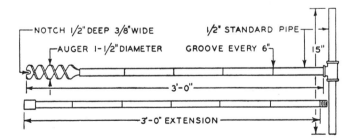

Fig. A—Soil Auger and Extension.

NOTCH 1/2" DEEP 3/8" WIDE   1/2" STANDARD PIPE

AUGER 1-1/2" DIAMETER   GROOVE EVERY 6"   15"

3'-0"

3'-0" EXTENSION

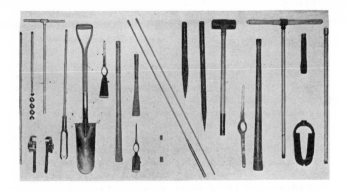

Fig. B—*Soil survey equipment.*

Fig. C—*Hydraulic boring equipment.*

amount of supplemental information such as geologic maps or soil keys is available for preliminary study of the site, the essential terrain information should be obtained by field reconnaissance. The soils observed along roads in the vicinity of the proposed highway should be studied and changes in the soil profile noted as they occur in highway cuts. These notes should include a complete description of the soil profile for each soil type observed. A correlation of this information with the type of parent material, the range in slope, the topographic position, the drainage conditions, and the land form or airphoto soil pattern can be used to establish a system for the identification of different soil types occurring in the area. It will be found that similar soil conditions may be encountered where similar soil profile characteristics exist; that changes in soil conditions accompany similar changes in parent material and relief; and that similar soil conditions have similar airphoto soil patterns for regions where no appreciable changes occur in climate or vegetation.

It may be desirable to prepare a preliminary strip map covering the area in which the road is to be located. In complex terrain, especially if adverse ground conditions exist, such a map will be useful in establishing preliminary lines for location work. Usually such maps are made on an airphoto base prepared from airphoto enlargements. Correlation of airphoto soil patterns with soil types and parent materials from geologic maps supplemented with limited ground reconnaissance should enable the engineer to prepare a reconnaissance soil map showing the distribution of the major soil conditions likely to be encountered during the detailed soil survey. In many instances, adverse ground conditions can be avoided by locating the highway through terrain which has more favorable soil conditions from the standpoint of current design practice. This map if prepared on the proper scale can later be converted into a detailed engineering soil map by accurately locating all auger borings and soil boundaries determined during the detailed survey made for the road location selected in the area.

Exploration of the Road Site

5. The field work for this phase of the soil survey consists of making examinations of the soils by means of auger borings, test pits or road cuttings. There is no definite rule to follow except that the soil profile should be examined at close enough intervals to determine the boundaries of each significant soil type occurring on the project. Borings should be made deep enough to determine if bedrock, adverse ground (peat or muck) or water conditions are apt to be encountered during the construction of the proposed road. After the boundaries of each soil type are established, sampling sites are selected so that representative samples can be obtained for laboratory test purposes.

When the boring must be extended to a depth of more than a few feet, a preliminary exploration by geophysical methods (see note) may reduce the required number of borings. This type of exploration is particularly applicable where the material to be excavated is rocky, gravelly, or cemented, in which case it is desirable to make only sufficient borings to obtain representative samples for testing. Geophysical methods may also be of value in exploration for surfacing aggregate and base course or borrow materials for the determination of either the location of a possible source of suitable material or lateral or vertical extent of a known source.

NOTE: A description of seismic and electrical resistivity methods, including discussions of relative merits of both methods can be found in the following references:

Geophysical Methods of Subsurface Exploration in Highway Construction, by R. W. Moore, Public Roads, Vol. 26, No. 3, Aug. 1950.

Application of Geology and Seismology to Highway Location and Design in Massachusetts, by G. H. Delano, L. W. Currier, and Rev. Daniel Lineham, pp. 66 to 91, Bulletin No. 18, Highway Research Board, 1948.

Geophysical Methods of Subsurface Exploration Applied to Material Surveys (with bibliography of 51 references), by R. W. Moore, Bulletin 62, Highway Research Board, 1952.

The following suggestions should assist the engineer in the preparation of the detailed soil survey. Modifications other than those indicated may be required to handle special conditions which are not encountered in the average highway soil survey:

(a) Spacing of Borings.—The spacing of borings should vary with the uniformity of the soil profile,[3] that is, with respect to the sequence and number of soil layers; the thickness, color, texture, consistency and structure of each soil layer; the chemical composition; the type of parent material, and the topography.

A convenient interval such as even stations may be assumed at the beginning if preliminary information is not available. This interval may be varied under the following conditions: (1) If the soil profile is uniform the interval may be increased; (2) when the character of the soil profile changes, intermediate borings should be made until it is clear that all variations have been mapped; (3) where the topography is rolling and the grade changes rapidly from cut to fill, detailed borings are necessary only in cuts; (4) where the original ground line or old grade is to be covered with fill material, no examination is necessary except to determine the character of the support. If fill material is to be ob-

3 References should be made to the following publications for details covering soil profile characteristics of various soil types occurring in the United States:
(1) Soils of the United States, by C. F. Marbut, U. S. Dept. of Agri., Atlas of American Agri., Part III, 1955.
(2) Soils and Men. Yearbook of Agriculture 1938, U. S. Department of Agriculture.
(3) Soil Survey Manual Handbook No. 18, U. S. Department of Agriculture, August 1951.

tained from borrow ditches along the road, the soil should be examined for the entire depth and extent of the borrow.

(b) Depth of Borings.—All borings should generally be carried to a depth of at least 3 ft. below the proposed grade line. The depths may vary according to the following stipulations: (1) When the road lies within uniform layers of the soil profile, the borings should extend down to the first layer below the ditchline which would block percolation, or through the pervious layer which would carry water; (2) When fill material is to be borrowed from ditches along the road, the borings should extend to the estimated depth of borrow; (3) In the study of frost action, the borings should extend to the mean depth of frost in those materials showing a high affinity for frost accumulation; and (4) When the location line follows an existing road, the soils may be mapped by examining the exposed cuts, but supplemental borings should be made in areas showing adverse pavement performance. In these road sections the borings should be made at least 3 ft. below pavement grade.

(e) Recording Boring Information. —A complete and systematic record of all boring and test pit examinations should be kept in a note book for each road project survey. The description of the site should give the project identification and the location of each test pit or auger boring, the location and identification of each sample taken for laboratory analysis, the nature of the ground, the origin of the parent material and landform. Whenever possible, the agricultural soil name should be given for future correlation purposes. The description of the

TEXTURE CLASSIFICATION OF SOILS

Soil Texture	Visual detection of Particle Size and general appearance of the soil	Squeezed in hand and pressure released — When Air Dry	Squeezed in hand and pressure released — When Moist	Soil ribboned between thumb and finger when moist.
Sand	Soil has a granular appearance in which the individual grain sizes can be detected. It is free-flowing when in a dry condition.	Will not form a cast and will fall apart when pressure is released.	Forms a cast which will crumble when lightly touched.	Can not be ribboned.
Sandy Loam	Essentially a granular soil with sufficient silt and clay to make it somewhat coherent. Sand characteristics predominate.	Forms a cast which readily falls apart when lightly touched.	Forms a cast which will bear careful handling without breaking.	Can not be ribboned.
Loam	A uniform mixture of sand, silt and clay. Grading of sand fraction quite uniform from coarse to fine. It is mellow, has somewhat gritty feel, yet is fairly smooth and slightly plastic.	Forms a cast which will bear careful handling without breaking.	Forms a cast which can be handled freely without breaking.	Can not be ribboned.
Silt Loam	Contains a moderate amount of the finer grades of sand and only a small amount of clay over half of the particles are silt. When dry it may appear quite cloddy which readily can be broken and pulverized to a powder.	Forms a cast which can be freely handled. Pulverized it has a soft flourlike feel.	Forms a cast which can be freely handled. When wet, soil runs together and puddles.	It will not ribbon but it has a broken appearance, feels smooth and may be slightly plastic.
Silt	Contains over 80% of silt particles with very little fine sand and clay. When dry, it may be cloddy; readily pulverizes to powder with a soft flourlike feel.	Forms a cast which can be handled without breaking.	Forms a cast which can freely be handled. When wet, it readily puddles.	It has a tendency to ribbon with a broken appearance, feels smooth.
Clay Loam	Fine textured soil breaks into hard lumps when dry. Contains more clay than silt loam. Resembles clay in a dry condition; identification is made on physical behavior of moist soil.	Forms a cast which can be freely handled without breaking.	Forms a cast which can be handled freely without breaking. It can be worked into a dense mass.	Forms a thin ribbon which readily breaks, barely sustaining its own weight.
Clay	Fine textured soil breaks into very hard lumps when dry. Difficult to pulverize into a soft flourlike powder when dry. Identification based on cohesive properties of the moist soil.	Forms a cast which can be freely handled without breaking.	Forms a cast which can be handled freely without breaking.	Forms long, thin flexible ribbons. Can be worked into a dense, compact mass. Considerable plasticity.
Organic Soils	Identification based on the high organic content. Muck consists of thoroughly decomposed organic material with considerable amount of mineral soil finely divided with some fibrous remains. When considerable fibrous material is present, it may be classified as peat. The plant remains or sometimes the woody structure can easily be recognized. Soil color ranges from brown to black. They occur in lowlands, in swamps or swales. They have high shrinkage upon drying.			

—Eighth Edition of Methods of Sampling and Testing AASHO

Table A—Field Method for Identification of Soil Texture

GRANULAR   **PLATY**

BLOCKY   **PRISMATIC**

Fig. D—*Four basic types of soil structure.*

Photos by Dr. Roy W. Simonson

soil material observed from the boring should include the field soil profile description, that is, the number, sequence, and thickness of each soil layer. Each soil layer should be described according to texture (see Page x), structure (see figure D), organic content, relative moisture content, and degree of cementation. The boring record should indicate the location of seepage zones, the position of free water table if it occurs in the auger boring, the bedrock contact and the nature and type of bedrock penetrated by the test boring. Table B indicates a typical boring record for a soil survey.

(d) *Mapping the Soil Profile.*— The data obtained from boring records and soil profile studies should be plotted on the prepared profile sheet to assist in making design recommendations. Several methods of recording such data are indicated by figures E and F.

One method is to establish the range of soil profile characteristics for each soil type (map unit) identified during the soil survey and indicate the boundaries of the different soil types on a plan view of a strip map including the proposed highway location. The location of auger borings, points where test samples were taken and supplemental notes on drainage, landform or soil types usually are included to furnish additional details affecting highway design. Usually a profile sketch is prepared in addition to the plan view to show subsurface information which is likely to influence the position of the grade line.

Another method is to prepare a detailed soil profile showing the location of each significant soil layer observed during the examination of test borings made on the project.

This type of soil profile should usually be prepared for complex terrain conditions such as soundings over peat swamps, or through topography which require numerous deep cuts and high fills to maintain satisfactory road alignment. For additional details on mapping soil profiles, reference should be made to the following literature.[4, 5, 6, 7]

(e) *Selection of Soil Samples.*—A 25-lb. sample of soil should be obtained from each soil layer with a pick and shovel from an exposed back slope, or from a test pit selected on the basis of a study of auger boring records. Each sample should be placed in a canvas bag, marked with adequate identification, tied securely and shipped to the laboratory. A sufficient number of samples should be taken to establish the range in test results for what appears to be the same soil layer.

Laboratory Tests

6. The samples of soil obtained during the field survey are submitted for laboratory test. The usual tests are those required for identification and classification purposes. These tests consist of the mechanical analysis, liquid limit, plastic limit, and compaction. In certain cases strength tests may be required to determine the suitability of soils and soil mixtures for base and wearing courses.

4 "The Soil Profile and Subgrade Survey," by W. I. Watkins and Henry Aaron, PUBLIC ROADS, Vol. 12, No. 7, 1951.

5 "Field Manual of Soil Engineering," Michigan State Highway Department, Lansing, Michigan. Third edition, revised 1952.

6 "Soils Manual," Missouri State Highway Commission, Bureau of Materials, Jefferson City, Missouri, 1948.

7 "Soils and Base Materials Survey," State Highway Commission of Kansas, January 1949.

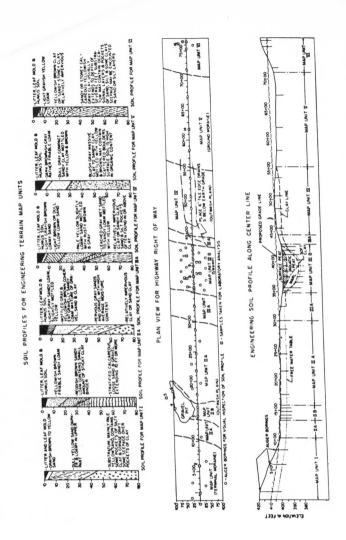

Fig. E—Example of soil profile mapping

— 26 —

Analysis of Data

7. Recommendations for the engineering use of a soil should be based on both the physical and environmental characteristics. In some instances the known behavior of similar soils observed during previous construction and pavement behavior studies can be effectively used to appraise the engineering use of the soils for design purposes. Often standard design cross sections can be established for significant soil types (map units). These need only a slight modification to make them suitable for soil conditions observed during a soil survey.

Subgrade Survey of an Existing Road

8. The section for study having been selected, the survey should be carried out as follows:

(a) The section should be staked out, the original construction stations being used, if possible. Arbitrary stations will serve the purpose when it is not convenient to locate original stations.

(b) Cross sections should be taken every 50 ft. along the centerline, or more often if topography requires, and for a distance of approximately 150 feet on each side of the centerline. Elevations should be taken with an engineer's level to the nearest 0.1 ft. The accuracy of the engineer's level is necessary for the construction of centerline and bankline profiles, but a hand level is sufficiently accurate for the topography adjacent to the highway. An assumed elevation may be used as a bench mark.

(c) A plan of the roadway should be drawn to a scale of 50 feet to the inch showing the type of pavement, type of failure, portion of roadway, which is built over an

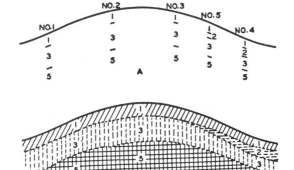

SCALES
HORIZONTAL — 1 INCH = 50 FEET
VERTICAL   — 1 INCH = 5 FEET

Fig. F—Example of soil profile mapping, illustrating the determination of limits of intermediate layers by supplemental borings.

— 27 —

older road, if any, and special construction.

(d) Cross section notes should be plotted to the same scale as the plan of roadway and contours drawn in by interpolation.

(e) The bank line profiles should be drawn on cross section paper using a horizontal scale of 50 ft. to the inch. The centerline profile and the grade line of the pre-existing road, if any, should be projected upon the bank line profiles.

(f) Soils should be mapped from soil profile characteristics in the same manner as suggested in section 5. The desired information may be conveniently obtained and recorded in the following manner:

(1) Scrape down the back slopes so that the original soil profile is exposed and plot the limits of the various layers on the prepared profile sheets. The soil profile should be examined by auger borings to a depth of at least 3 to 5 ft. below the centerline grade. This depth will vary with the uniformity of the soil layers or soil material. Any variations in moisture content and density should be specially noted. Obtain the elevations of the limits of the different layers in exposed back slopes by means of a

Table B—Typical boring record for soil survey purposes.

Patent material: Nearly level red shale

Topography: Rolling

Land use: Meadow

Agronomic soil series: Unknown

Airphoto No.: 117-57

Project: 71-2-509

Date: May 23, 1948

Operator: R. Sims

Test hole: M-7

Boring location: Sta. 50+90, 25 ft. Rt.

Remarks: Natural surface drainage to west, drainage good—erosion active on unprotected slopes

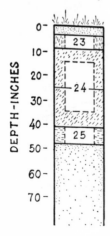

0 to 4"—Heavy sod and vines.

4 to 9"—Brownish red silty clay—friable and dry.

9 to 25"—Brownish red clay, firm but friable, breaking down to a granular structure.

25 to 41"—Very red silty clay, quite compact.

41 to 48"—Hard brittle red clay (almost rotten rock).

48" + —Hard rotten red shale.

Remarks: A chisel was required to remove material from 41" to 48" depth.

In-place density taken between 16 and 24".

Test samples Nos. 23 taken at 4 to 9" depth

24 taken at 15 to 36" depth

25 taken at 41 to 48" depth

hand level, the elevation of the centerline being used as a bench mark.

(2) Describe the profile in a separate notebook noting the details of each soil layer according to the properties enumerated in section 5.

(3) Examine the soil every 50 ft. or less, depending upon the uniformity of the soil profile.

(4) On the plan of the roadway plot the limits of the various soil layers found directly under the surfacing material. When the roadway is cut through uniform layers of soil material, the limits are obtained by constructing cross sections from the bank line profiles. When the roadway is constructed of fill material or cut through a heterogeneous soil material, the limits are determined by soil auger borings in the shoulder.

(5) Adequate samples should be taken from each significant soil layer as described in section 5.

(6) Photographs should be taken illustrating the condition of the pavement, the shoulders, the back slopes, the ditches, and the appearance of the soil layers.

(g) *Analysis of Data.*—The data collected in the manner described above should be analysed, together with the laboratory test data, and information on the following subjects developed:

(1) The relation that exists between pavement condition, the field characteristics of the soil, and the physical properties of the soil as determined in the laboratory.

(2) The possible reasons for failure.

(3) Possible corrective measures for the case under examination.

(4) Preventive measures which may be applied in the future.

Special Problems

9. The elevation of the water table, the exploration of swamps, the location of bedrock, and the determination of the magnitude of underground seepage are usually treated as special problems during the course of making a highway soils survey.

(a) *Water Table.*—If no trace of soil moisture is observed in an auger boring or test pit, it may be backfilled at once, but if water is found or indicated, the boring or test pit should be left open for 12 to 24 hours to allow the water to rise to its final level so that its true position can be recorded. When a boring pierces an impervious layer resting upon a porous layer in which water is under pressure, special drainage may be required and it is advisable to make a detailed study of the area. In all instances where free water is encountered, additional borings should be made nearby to check the magnitude and extent of the water condition. It is good practice to plot all information on the site showing water table contours or profiles depending upon the nature of the field examination. The mottled color of the subsoil will assist in the identification of areas which may have a fluctuating water table, especially if the mottling consists of gray and blue colorations interspersed with brown, yellow or rust colorations. Certain types of vegetation such as rushes, willows, tamarac, etc., are indicators of high ground water conditions. The presence or absence of indicator vegetation can be used effectively to determine if seasonal high water table conditions are likely to occur in the area being surveyed.

(b) *Bedrock.*—The determination of the location and elevation of bedrock usually requires a detailed site study. Sufficient borings should be made to accurately outline the bedrock contact occurring in all road cuts. Samples of the bedrock should be examined to determine the uniformity and nature of the underlying rock. It may be desirable in areas containing variable depths to bedrock to explore the area by geophysical methods to determine the most advantageous locations for checking depth to bedrock. All rock outcrops and borings or test pits used to determine the depth to bedrock should be recorded on the soil profile drawings.

(c) *Soundings of Swamps.*—The soundings greater than normal auger depth (approximately 6 ft.) should be made with a Davis Peat Sampler or its equivalent. This sampler permits taking samples at any depth. The location of soundings varies with the type of material encountered and the depth of the swamp being examined. If swamp conditions are uniform, the soundings can be taken at longer intervals (100 ft. maximum) than in swamps with deep pockets and wide variations in material. For average swamp conditions soundings at 50-foot intervals along the centerline and 25 feet to the right and left for a distance of 100 feet should be sufficient. If there is an appreciable difference in the depth of swamp material between 50 ft. intervals, the boundaries of the change should be established by additional soundings. When making soundings, samples should be taken at 4-ft. vertical intervals, and in case of a change in the nature of the material, the transition should be noted in the profile drawings.

In case the swamp is large and further deep soundings are necessary, it may be advisable to make a note on the soil map to the effect that additional soundings should be made later rather than delay the soil survey.

All pot holes and small valleys, meander scars, especially in a glaciated area should be examined to locate any buried muck deposits. A study of airphoto soil patterns should assist in the identification of areas likely to contain adverse ground conditions. Attention is called to the fact that peat and muck deposits are not always associated with depressions but may also occur on sidehills or benches in glaciated areas and in mountainous regions with high rainfall.

3.03 AIDS TO THE SOIL SURVEY

Two important aids to the soil survey have, during the past few years, grown in importance to the soils engineer and soils technician. They are (1) the pedological classification system in conjunction with agricultural soil maps and (2) aerial photographs. These aids to the soil survey are discussed briefly in this manual.

3.04 PEDOLOGICAL CLASSIFICATION SYSTEM

Pedology, or soil science, is defined as "the science that treats of soils, including their nature, properties, formation, functioning, behavior, and response to use and management."* The pedological classification system is used in the development of agricultural soil maps. This system of classification of soils originated in Russia about 1870 and is based on the premise that a soil's structure, form, and properties are determined or controlled by five factors acting in combination. These factors are (1) parent material, (2) climate, (3) relief, (4) vegetation, and (5) age.

The original Russian classification system has undergone numerous changes and refinements. Agricultural soil scientists in the United States have, during the past fifty years, taken an active part in improving this system.

3.05 SUBDIVISION INTO CATEGORIES

The present system of pedological classification first divides soils into three orders (Table III-1). These three orders are zonal, intrazonal and azonal. The zonal order includes those soils having well-developed profiles† that reflect the dominating influence of climate and vegetation. The intrazonal order includes those soils having essentially well-developed profiles that reflect the dominating influence of some local factor, such as relief, parent material, or age over the normal effects of climate and vegetation. In contrast to the zonal order, they normally occur over rather small areas. The azonal, or immature, order includes those soils without well-developed

---

* "Soil Survey Manual," U. S. Dept. of Agriculture, Handbook No. 18, Aug. 1951.

† *Soil profile*—a vertical section through the deposit extending from the surface into the parent material.

Table III-1—Classification of Soils on the Basis of Their Characteristics

Category VI Order	Category V Suborder*	Category IV Great soil groups*	Category III Family*	Category II Series*	Category I Type*
Zonal soils	1. Light-colored soils of arid regions	1. Desert soils	Mesa	Mesa	Mesa gravelly loam
				Chipeta	Chipeta silty clay loam
		2. Red Desert soils	Mohave	Mohave	Mohave loam
		3. Sierozem	Portneuf	Reeves	Reeves fine sandy loam
				Portneuf	Portneuf silt loam
		4. Brown soils	Joplin	Joplin	Joplin loam
				Weld	Weld loam
		5. Reddish Brown soils	Springer	Springer	Springer fine sandy loam
				White House	White House coarse sandy loam
	2. Light-colored podzolic soils of the timbered regions	6. Brown Podzolic soils	Gloucester	Gloucester	Gloucester loam
					Gloucester sandy loam
				Merrimac	Merrimac sandy loam
					Merrimac loamy sand
		7. Gray-Brown Podzolic soils	Miami	Miami	Miami silt loam
				Fox	Fox silt loam
				Bellefontaine	Bellefontaine loam
			Plainfield	Plainfield	Plainfield loamy sand
				Coloma	Coloma loamy sand
			Chester	Chester	Chester loam
				Frederick	Frederick silt loam
			Porters	Porters	Porters loam
Intrazonal soils	1. Hydromorphic soils of marshes, swamps, seep areas, and flats				

2. Calomorphic	1. Brown Forest soils (Braunerde) 2. Rendzina soils	Brooke Burton Houston Aguilita	Brooke Burton Houston Soller Bell Aguilita Diablo	Brooke clay loam Burton loam Houston clay Soller clay loam Bell clay Aguilita clay Diablo clay
Azonal soils	1. Lithosols	Underwood Muskingum Dekalb Wabash Laurel Sharkey Genesee Gila Hanford	Underwood McCammon Muskingum Dekalb Wabash Cass Laurel Sarpy Sharkey Genesee Huntington Gila Pima Hanford Yolo	Underwood stony loam McCammon loam Muskingum stony silt loam Dekalb stony loam Wabash clay loam Cass loam Laurel fine sandy loam Sarpy very fine sandy loam Sharkey clay Genesee silt loam Huntington silt loam Gila very fine sandy loam Pima silty clay loam Hanford loam Yolo loam
	2. Alluvial soils			
	3. Sands (dry)			

* Suborders, great soil groups, families, series, and types listed are intended only as examples to illustrate the system of classification. When all of the soils of the United States (and of the world as a whole) are studied and classified, several more suborders, even more great soil groups, many more families, a few thousand series, and thousands of local soil types will have to be recognized.

soil profiles. Active sand dune areas and recent alluvial or flood plain soils are examples.

The three orders are further subdivided into *suborders*, as shown in Table III-1. The suborders are then divided into *great soil groups* which reflect the combined effect of climate, vegetation, and topography. These three subdivisions (orders, suborders, and great soil groups) comprise the higher categories of the pedological system. For the highway or airport engineer working in a given region, these three higher categories, normally, are of minor interest for they ordinarily do not appear on the agricultural soil map.

Basic to this system of classification is the nature and condition of the weathered soil profile. Such factors as age, climate, relief, and vegetation play an important role in shaping or determining the characteristics of this profile. It has been observed that a vertical section (profile) through most soils can be divided into zones called horizons. Normally only three horizons are recognized or dealt with. They are (1) the A horizon which lies at the surface and is the zone from which material (minerals and colloids) is being removed by leaching, (2) the B horizon is the zone of accumulation where the material leached from the A horizon is normally deposited; and (3) the C horizon or parent material which is much less weathered and from which the A and B horizons developed. Occasionally a fourth horizon, D, is included and frequently the A and B horizons are subdivided as shown in Figure III-1.

By carefully observing such soil profile features as the number, color, texture, structure, arrangement, chemical composition, and thickness of the various horizons, as well as the geology of the soil material, agricultural soil scientists have been able to subdivide the great soil groups into *soil series*. A series consists of a group of soils which have developed from the same kind of parent material, and by the same combination of soil forming processes.

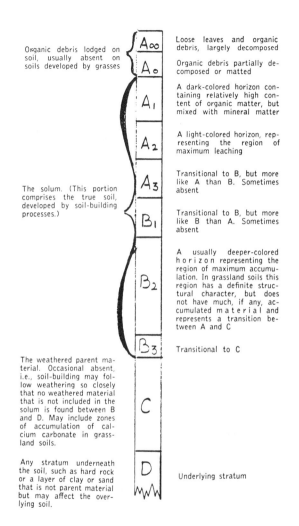

Organic debris lodged on soil, usually absent on soils developed by grasses

A_{oo} — Loose leaves and organic debris, largely decomposed

A_o — Organic debris partially decomposed or matted

A_1 — A dark-colored horizon containing relatively high content of organic matter, but mixed with mineral matter

A_2 — A light-colored horizon, representing the region of maximum leaching

The solum. (This portion comprises the true soil, developed by soil-building processes.)

A_3 — Transitional to B, but more like A than B. Sometimes absent

B_1 — Transitional to B, but more like B than A. Sometimes absent

B_2 — A usually deeper-colored horizon representing the region of maximum accumulation. In grassland soils this region has a definite structural character, but does not have much, if any, accumulated material and represents a transition between A and C

B_3 — Transitional to C

The weathered parent material. Occasional absent, i.e., soil-building may follow weathering so closely that no weathered material that is not included in the solum is found between B and D. May include zones of accumulation of calcium carbonate in grassland soils.

C

Any stratum underneath the soil, such as hard rock or a layer of clay or sand that is not parent material but may affect the overlying soil.

D — Underlying stratum

Figure III-1—A Hypothetical Soil Profile Having the Principal Horizons. No One Soil Would be Expected to Have all These Horizons Well-Developed, but Every Soil has Some of Them.
—From: "Soils & Men," Yearbook of Agriculture 1938, U. S. Dept. of Agriculture.

The horizons of a given series, except for the texture of the A horizons, are quite similar in their arrangement and general characteristics. Many of the first series mapped in the United States were given the names of towns, rivers, or counties near the spot where the soil series was first observed. Such series names as Hagerstown, Fargo, and Miami are typical.

Table III-1 shows that many of the soil series are grouped together in *families*. For example the Miami family includes the Miami, Bellefontaine, Hillsdale, Russell, Fox, and similar soils which are closely related. Generally speaking there has been no consistent grouping of soil series into well-defined families and, for the highway engineer, this grouping into families is, currently, of little importance. However, a grouping of soil series into *catenas* is of somewhat greater interest to the highway engineer. A catena is defined as a group of soil series within a given area which have been derived from similar parent materials but occupy different slope positions. For example, the Miami, Crosby, Brookston, and Clyde soil series frequently occur together on rolling and undulating to level terrain in the Late Wisconsin Drift area. The Miami soils occupy the higher and steeper slope positions, whereas the Clyde soils occur in deep depressions. These four soils have been grouped together into a catena.

Although the soil series is the basic (and most common) soil unit with which the soils engineer or technician normally works, a cursory examination of Table III-1 will show that even the soil series is further subdivided into soil *types*. A given soil series is divided into types on the basis of the texture of the surface soil (A horizon) which is normally about six to eight inches in thickness. The texture of the A horizon is frequently determined by visual inspection but may require a sieve analysis in some cases. Once the percentages of sand, silt, and clay present in a given sample are known, one can refer to a chart such as Figure III-2 to determine the soil type name. Such type names as sandy-clay-loam, clay-loam, and silty clay are common.

In retrospect one will note that the pedological system divides soils into a number of categories called *orders, suborders, great soil groups, families, series,* and *types.* For the highway engineer, only the last two categories (series and type) are of great importance, for only these two normally appear on soil maps.

3.06 AGRICULTURAL SOIL MAPS

Since 1899 the Soil Survey Division of the United States Department of Agriculture has prepared and published soil maps and bulletins. (See Figure III-3.) Much land area of the United States now has been surveyed. These bulletins, with maps, can be examined by the public at university and public libraries or obtained directly from the Department of Agriculture or its local representatives.

Normally the surveys cover a one-county area, and the Committee on Surveying, Mapping, and Classification of Soils of the Highway Research Board has compiled

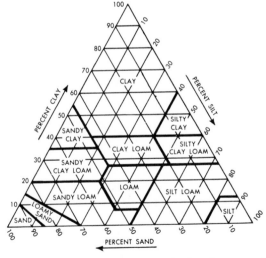

Figure III-2—Guide for the Textural Classification of Soil (U. S. Dept. of Agriculture Soil Conservation Service)

Figure III-3—Section of Soil Map from Soil Survey Bulletin

a list of counties in the United States which have been or are being mapped. The first such tabulation appeared as Highway Research Board Bulletin No. 22 in 1949 and was entitled "Engineering Use of Agricultural Soil Maps." More recent bulletins (HRB Bulletin Nos. 28, 46, 65, and 83) sponsored by this Highway Research Committee have listed the county soil surveys completed or in progress since 1949.

Since these soil survey maps have been prepared over a period of several years and numerous changes and refinements in the method and techniques of conducting the surveys and classifying the soils have been made in this interval, the older maps are often not as complete, detailed, and correct as more recent ones. Consequently, the Department of Agriculture has developed a numerical rating system based upon the accuracy and completeness of these maps. Ratings range from 1 to 4 with the number 1 rating being the best. The Highway Research Bulletins mentioned above include this rating with each survey listed.

3.07 PRECAUTIONS

The soils engineer, or technician, who plans to use Agricultural Soil Maps must realize that these maps, at best, are only a tool which can be used as a general guide to assist him in planning and conducting an engineering soil survey. Agricultural soil mapping is superficial, the depth of soil examined being about three feet. The scale to which these maps normally are drawn does not permit the showing of certain details which are frequently important to the engineer. For example, if, within a given soil area, a small area of other soils (series or type) is present, and these soils are similar agriculturally, they are not identified generally unless they represent more than 10 or 15 percent of the soil area in which they are included. Generally, soils from the same horizon and same soil series will exhibit similar engineering properties within acceptable limits. There are, of course, exceptions to this rule. The soils engineer must obtain sufficient samples and perform the necessary tests to minimize the possibility of this exception going unnoticed.

In spite of these and other drawbacks, the pedological soil classification system and agricultural soil maps undoubtedly will become increasingly important and useful to the soils engineer.

B. Air Photo Interpretation

3.08 GENERAL

A thorough description of the air photo interpretation method as it applies to mapping soil areas is beyond the scope of this manual. Nevertheless, some of the basic concepts and some of the merits and limitations of this method will be discussed here. Soils engineers and technicians who wish to learn more about identifying and mapping soils by means of air photos should obtain and study the numerous bulletins on the subject which have been prepared by staff members at Purdue, Cornell, and other universities. Graduate, undergraduate and short intensive courses in the subject are available at some universities. Formal training of this type is necessary and helpful for individuals who want to become expert in this field.

3.09 BASIC PRINCIPLES

Three principles which are basic to the identification of soils by means of aerial photographs are listed below.

(1) An aerial photograph reproduces accurately the physical features of the earth's surface, and records not only natural but man-made features as well (Figure III-4). In so doing, the photograph records the results of natural processes which have been active in the development of residual soils and the occurrence of transported soils by reflecting surface and subsurface features.

Figure III-4—Contrast Between Natural and Man-Made Features, Lancaster Co., Pa.—*Courtesy, U. S. Dept. of Agriculture*

Figure III-5—Unlike Materials Produce Unlike Patterns:—Limestone (left) and Shale (right), in Berkeley Co., W. Va.—*Courtesy, U. S. Dept. of Agriculture*

Figure III-6—Loess Soil in Iowa (above) Reveals a Pattern in Aerial Photograph Strikingly Similar to that of Mississippi Loess (below)—*Courtesy, U. S. Dept. of Agriculture*

(2) Similar materials reflect similar air photo patterns and unlike materials reproduce unlike patterns (Figure III-5). Because of this, surface and subsurface features can be grouped together in patterns

which are unique for a given type of soil and environment.

(3) Soil patterns as reflected by air photos are repetitive in nature. For example, the soils of Iowa are simular to the soils of the Ukraine. Furthermore, the air photo patterns are quite similar for these two areas.

3.10 ELEMENTS OF THE SOIL PATTERN

The factors which the interpreter uses in air photo studies have been called elements of the soil pattern. There are natural elements or factors such as land form, vegetation, soil color, drainage system, gully system, gully shape, and erosion features. There are man-made elements such as land use, field pattern, erosion and drainage control, and highway and railway grade and alignment.

At times a single element may dominate a pattern and become the chief guide by which the interpreter determines the soil type. Generally speaking, however, the soil type is determined by a study of the combined elements.

Once all of these elements have been studied and evaluated, the trained air photo interpreter can frequently determine the nature and extent of the various soils in a given area. Where the areas under study are accessible, field soil surveys should always be made to supplement, prove, and correct or adjust the original air photo predictions.

3.11 CHOICE AND AVAILABILITY OF AERIAL PHOTOGRAPHS

Large areas of the United States have been photographed by various agencies, and in many cases these photographs are both suitable and available for air photo studies. A map entitled *Aerial Photography of the United States* may be obtained from the Director, Geological

Survey, Washington 25, D. C. The latest edition of this map will show the areas of the United States which have been photographed and the agencies holding the aerial photographs. Further information about ordering photographs can be obtained from the agencies concerned. Frequently an index sheet giving the identification numbers for individual photographs is first obtained for an area. The necessary prints are then ordered after the specific locality has been located on the index sheet.

Contact prints which are either 9 by 18, 7 by 9, or 9 by 9 inches are available in stereo-pairs. The scale of the photographs should lie between 1:15,000 and 1:22,000 for normal usage. Simple stereoscopes which permit a considerable amount of magnification can be used to study pairs of photographs.

3.12 LIMITATIONS

Although this method of identifying and mapping soils can be a valuable tool to the soils engineer, it has certain limitations, and these must be kept in mind. Two of the more obvious limitations are:

In built-up areas where buildings and structures cover a large portion of the area, it is usually most difficult to use the air photos successfully for soils studies.

It should be remembered that the photograph records only those features which are at the surface. This is usually a greater handicap for the foundation engineer than the highway and airport engineer. In some instances, however, the surface features reflect quite well the nature of soil deposits to considerable depths. Where this is not the case, this limitation frequently can be overcome by a careful study of gully shapes and gradients. These gullies frequently knife deeply into a deposit and expose its interior for examination by the photo interpreter.

These as well as other limitations are present in this method, yet its importance to highway and airport soil engineers will continue to grow in the future.

Chapter IV

SIGNIFICANCE OF TESTS ON SOIL MATERIALS

4.01 GENERAL

Highway and airport engineers and soil technicians are acquainted with the basic tests performed in soils laboratories. Frequently, however, the acquaintance is superficial because of lack of experience with the tests. Many technicians are quite skillful in performing the tests but cannot interpret the results. The American Society of Civil Engineers published, in the September, 1957, issue of the *Journal of the Highway Division*, a progress report on "Significance of Tests for Highway Materials—Basic Tests."* This report was prepared so that those using the tests could appreciate the significance of the results.

Because it is important to know the significance of tests as well as the mechanics of performing them, three of the tests on soils described in the ASCE report are included in the following paragraphs. They are (1) the mechanical analysis, (2) consistency tests and indices, and (3) the moisture-density test. The test for specific gravity, not included in the ASCE report, also is described in this chapter.

A. Mechanical Analysis
(Sieve and Hydrometer Analyses)
ASTM Test Designation: D 422
AASHO Test Designation: T 88

4.02 SIGNIFICANCE OF TEST

The *mechanical analysis* of a soil is the determination of the percent of individual grain sizes present in the sample.

The results of the tests are of most value when used for classification purposes. Further use of the gradation should be discouraged unless verification by studies of performance or experience permit empirical

---

* "Significance of Tests for Highway Materials-Basic Tests: Progress Report of the Committee on Significance of Tests for Highway Materials of the Highway Division," Paper No. 1385, *Journal of the Highway Division*, American Society of Civil Engineers, Sept. 1957.

formulae. Only rough approximations of strength or resistance properties should be attempted. Quite often it will be found that the larger
the grain size, the better are the engineering properties. Also, it is a
known fact that detrimental capillarity and frost damage are not a
problem with the coarse (sandy) material, whereas it can be very danger-
ous with the fine-grained silts and clays. Some empirical relationships have
been developed such as the criterion commonly used for determining the
susceptibility of soil to pumping under rigid pavements. Highway specifications for subbase and base materials also use the grain size analysis
for quality measurement.

For soil stabilization, use is frequently made of grain size analyses for
mix design and control. One criterion for bituminous stabilization is a
requirement for a minimum percent of sand and gravel size. The percent
of cement to be used in soil-cement mixtures can be estimated on the
basis of the grain size. For mechanical stabilization or aggregate bases
(well graded granular material with or without a chemical admixture)
the results of the gradation tests are used to determine the size and
percent of aggregates or fines that are needed for a dense, impermeable
material.

On occasion, the degree of permeability (measure of the amount of
water that will flow through a material) is estimated on the basis of
grain size. Here again, certain generalities are possible but accurate
estimates are not. The larger-grained soils will more readily permit the
flow of water than finer-grained ones, i.e., sands are more permeable
than silts, and silts are more permeable than clays. An example of the
variation from this generality is a well-graded, granular material which
can be sufficiently impermeable to serve as a core for an earth dam.

4.03 SYNOPSIS OF TEST METHODS

The mechanical analysis consists of two parts: one, the determination
of the amount of coarse material by the use of sieves or screens; and
two, the analysis for the fine-grained fraction commonly employing an
hydrometer analysis.

The sieve analysis is a simple test consisting of sieving a measured
quantity of material through successively smaller sieves. The weight
retained on each sieve is expressed as a percentage of the total sample.

The hydrometer analysis is conducted on a sample of the material that
passes a No. 200 sieve.* The test is based on the principle that the soil
can be dispersed uniformly through a liquid. The specific gravity of the
soil-liquid mixture is then measured at various time intervals. Stoke's
Law is used to compute the rate of settling of the various sizes; i.e., the
larger grains settle more rapidly than the smaller grains. The computations include corrections for temperature, viscosity of the liquid and the
specific gravity of the soil particles. The results are first expressed as a

---

* Note: AASHO Designation T88 and ASTM Designation D422 call for a
sample passing the No. 10 sieve.

percent of the sample used in the hydrometer analysis, and then converted to percentages of the total soil sample if there is a coarse grained fraction.

4.04 TYPICAL TEST RESULTS

The results of the mechanical analysis can be presented in either of two forms. One is a table in which there is listed the percentage of the total sample that will pass a given sieve size or is smaller than a specified grain diameter. The second form is a plot of the sieve number or grain size vs. the percentage passing the given sieve (smaller than the given diameter). For this latter form, grain size is normally plotted on a logarithmic plot due to the wide range in values, while the percentage finer is plotted on an arithmetic scale.

Nomenclature has been established for materials within certain grain-size limits. In decreasing order of size these groups are as follows:

> gravel, coarser than 2.0 mm. (No. 10 sieve)
> coarse sand, 2.0 - 0.6 mm. (No. 10 - No. 30)
> medium sand, 0.6 - 0.2 mm. (No. 30 - No. 80)
> fine sand, 0.2 mm. - 0.05 mm. (No. 80 - No. 270)
> silt, 0.05 - 0.005 mm.
> clay, finer than 0.005 mm.
> colloids, finer than 0.001 mm.

Soils designated as sandy will contain more than 50% sand or gravel size. Silty soils will contain from 40% to as great as 100% silt size. Clays will contain as low as 30% or as high as 100% clay and colloids. Gravelly soils will normally contain at least 15% gravel-size material.

NOTE: The grain size limits listed for the soil constituents by the ASCE committee do not agree with the limits established by the American Association of State Highway Officials and the American Society for Testing and Materials. The soil grain size limits as contained in AASHO Designation T 88 are as follows:

> Particles larger than 2.0mm (No. 10 sieve)
> Coarse Sand, 2.0mm to 0.42mm (No. 10 to No. 40)
> Fine Sand, 0.42mm to 0.74mm (No. 40 to No. 200)
> Silt, 0.074mm to 0.005mm (No. 200 to ----)
> Clay, smaller than .005mm
> Colloids, smaller than 0.001mm

ASTM Designation D 422 was revised in 1961 to the following grain size limits:

> Gravel, 3 inches to 4.76mm (3-inch sieve to No. 4 sieve)
> Coarse Sand, 4.76mm to 2.00mm (No. 4 to No. 10)
> Medium Sand, 2.00mm to 0.42mm (No. 10 to No. 40)
> Fine Sand, 0.42mm to 0.074mm (No. 40 to No. 200)
> Silt size, 0.074mm to 0.005mm (No. 200 to ---)
> Clay size, smaller than 0.005mm
> Colloids, smaller than 0.001mm

4.05 INFLUENCES OF THE METHODS OF TEST

For the sieve analysis, care must be taken to remove clay and silt that may be adhering to the sand and gravel. In preparing the sample for testing, one must avoid fracturing some types of soft gravel and stone particles. For the very fine sands (No. 100 or No. 200 sieves) it will be desirable to wash the sample through the sieves.

The hydrometer analysis is particularly susceptible to poor results due to technique. The following are major sources of error:

1. Improper deflocculation (failure to separate the material into individual grains).

2. Improper mixing of soil and liquid.

3. Careless placement and removal of the hydrometer.

Figure IV-1—Separated Soil After Sieving

B. Specific Gravity of Soils
AASHO Designation: T 100
ASTM Designation: D 854

4.06 SIGNIFICANCE OF TEST

The *specific gravity* of a soil is the ratio of the weight in air of a given volume of soil particles at a stated temperature to the weight in air of an equal volume of distilled water at a stated temperature. The specific gravity is used frequently in relating a weight of soil to its volume. The unit weight of moist soil—needed in most pressure, settlement, and stability problems—can be computed with known values for specific gravity, degree of saturation, and void ratio. The specific gravity is used in the computations of many laboratory tests on soils.

In many soils the presence of a number of minerals, each having a different specific gravity, may present difficulties. This is why the test method requires that the Method of Test for Specific Gravity and Absorption of Coarse Aggregate (AASHO Designation: T 85; ASTM Designation: C 127) be used for the coarse portion when the soil has material retained on the No. 4 sieve. The specific gravity for the soil then is determined from the weighted average of the values for the coarse and the fine portions, using the following formula:

$$\text{Combined specific gravity} = \frac{1}{\dfrac{pc}{gc} + \dfrac{pf}{gf}}$$

in which pc = percent of coarse portion expressed as a decimal
gc = specific gravity of coarse portion
pf = percent of fine portion expressed as a decimal
gf = specific gravity of fine portion

4.07 SYNOPSIS OF TEST METHOD

The prescribed weight of the sample (all passing the No. 4 sieve or the No. 10 sieve depending upon the purpose of the test) is placed carefully in a calibrated pycnometer. Distilled water is added to fill the flask about three-fourths full. The entrapped air in the soil then is removed by partial vacuum or by boiling. The calibrated pycnometer then is filled with distilled water and weighed. The specific gravity is computed, using the determined weights and temperature corrections.

4.08 TYPICAL TEST RESULTS

The specific gravities of soils range from below 2.0 for organic or porous particle soils to over 3.0 for soils containing heavy minerals. Most soils, however, have specific gravities in the range of 2.65 to 2.85. A soil containing different minerals can have a range of specific gravities, depending on the care used to obtain a representative sample.

4.09 INFLUENCES OF THE METHOD OF TEST

Accurate results depend upon extreme care in obtaining weight and temperature measurements. A small error may be quite significant in the results. Calibration of the pycnometers, complete removal of entrapped air, and drying of the samples should be done with precision.

C. Consistency Tests and Indices
(Atterberg Limits)

Liquid Limit	ASTM Designation	: D 423
	AASHO Designation	: T 89
Plastic Limit	ASTM Designation	: D 424
	AASHO Designation	: T 90
Shrinkage Limit	ASTM Designation	: D 427
	AASHO Designation	: T 92
Plasticity Index (PI)	ASTM Designation	: D 424
	AASHO Designation	: T 91

4.10 SIGNIFICANCE OF TEST

The *consistency* tests or the Atterberg Limits consist of the liquid limit, the plastic limit, and the shrinkage limit. A value frequently used in conjunction with these limits is the plasticity index. The engineering properties of soil vary with the amount of water present, and results of the three consistency tests, expressed as moisture contents, are arbitrarily used to differentiate between the various states of the material. The liquid limit is the moisture content at which the soil changes from the liquid to the plastic state. The plastic limit is the border between the plastic and semi-solid, and the shrinkage limit delineates the semi-solid from the solid state. The plasticity index is the arithmetic difference between the liquid and plastic limits; i.e., it is the range of moisture content over which a material is in the plastic state.

The most common application of the test results to highway problems is in soil classification with those soils with comparable limits and indices classed together. Generally, soils with high liquid limits are clays with poor engineering properties. A low plasticity index indicates a granular soil with little or no cohesion and plasticity. Both the liquid limit and the plasticity index are used to some degree as a quality measuring device for pavement materials, in order to exclude those granular materials with too many fine-grained particles that have cohesive plastic qualities.

During recent years, many laboratories have abandoned the use of the shrinkage limit. In the highway field, classification is most commonly made on the basis of the Highway Research Board system which requires the gradation, the liquid and plastic limits, and the plasticity index.

4.11 SYNOPSIS OF TEST METHODS

The liquid limit test consists of molding a soil pat in a brass cup, cutting a groove in the pat with a special cutting tool and dropping the cup onto a solid base from a constant height. The liquid limit is that moisture content at which the groove closes for a length of ½" under 25 impacts.

The plastic limit test consists of rolling a soil sample into a thin thread. The soil thread is made by rolling a wet sample on a plate with the hand. This procedure is repeated until the sample crumbles when the diameter of the thread is equal to ⅛". The moisture content of the soil in this latter condition is the plasfic limit of the soil.

The shrinkage limit is conducted by saturating a soil sample, placing the material in a small dish of known volume, and weighing. The specimen is then placed in an oven and dried to a constant weight. During the drying period, the sample shrinks and loses volume at a rate more or less proportionate to the volume of water evaporated until the shrinking stops abruptly. The shrinkage limit is the moisture content of the saturated sample at the time the shrinkage ceases.

4.12 TYPICAL TEST RESULTS

The liquid limit varies widely and values as high as 80 to 100 are not uncommon with values of 40 to 60 more typical for clay soils. For silty soils, values of 25 to 50 can be expected. The liquid limit test will not produce a result for a sandy soil, and the results are reported as "non-plastic."

The plastic limit of silts and clays will not vary too widely and will range from 5 to 30. Normally, the silty soils will have the lower plastic limit. Since a pure sand is non-plastic, the thin thread cannot be rolled and the material is termed "non-plastic." For the shrinkage limit, clays may range in values from 6 to 14, with silty materials most frequently showing values between 15 and 30. Pure sand will show no decrease in volume during the drying period.

The plasticity index can be as high as 70 to 80 for the very plastic clays. Commonly, clays will have P. I.'s between 20 and 40. The silty materials normally range in P. I. between 10 and 20. For quality evaluations, bases, sub-bases and subgrades are sometimes restricted to those materials with a liquid limit of 25 or less and a maximum P.I. of 6, i.e., a predominantly granular material.

4.13 INFLUENCES OF THE METHODS OF TESTS

For the liquid limit the most common sources of error include (1) inaccurate height of drop of the cup, (2) a worn cup due to scratching with the grooving tool, (3) too thick a soil pat, (4) the rate of dropping the cup and (5) the human element in deciding when the groove has closed ½".

In many laboratories where production is a major concern, the test is conducted using only one moisture content, taken when the material is considered to be at the liquid limit. In the standard method of test, at least three moisture contents are determined, one below the liquid limit, one at or near the liquid limit and the third higher than the liquid limit. The results are plotted by placing the moisture content on an arithmetic plot with the number of blows on a semi-log basis. This permits a more exact establishment of the liquid limit.

D. Moisture - Density Test
(Proctor Test)

ASTM Test Designation : D 698

AASHO Test Designation : T 99

4.14 SIGNIFICANCE OF TEST

The *moisture-density* test is designed specifically to aid in the field compaction of soils so as to develop the best engineering properties of the material. It is assumed that the strength or shearing resistance of the soil increases with higher densities. Thus, the test is designed to get the best results from the soil available.

The "standard" moisture-density test as conducted in the laboratory uses a constant laboratory compactive effort, and it is assumed that it is similar in magnitude to the weight, impact and action of the average construction equipment. As might be anticipated, a greater compactive effort will bring an increase in density, and such a procedure was followed in developing the so-called "modified" moisture-density test. Presumably, heavier construction equipment would be required to obtain the "modified" density than would be needed to get "standard" density.

Another important factor is that the presence of a certain amount of water is needed in order to get the densities desired. For simplicity, the water can be assumed to act as a lubricant. However, too much water tends to force the particles apart and the higher densities cannot be obtained. Therefore the laboratory test not only defines the density that should be obtained by the construction equipment, it also delineates how much water should be used during the compaction.

Given a density (termed maximum density) and the proper moisture content (termed optimum moisture content) the construction forces can compact the soil into the best condition practicable. As a check, field forces employ a density test to determine the density obtained by the construction equipment. If the results are lower than the values permitted by the specifications, the material should be recompacted.

Note: Since this discussion was prepared by the ASCE committee in 1957, the American Association of State Highway Officials and the American Society for Testing and Materials have adopted modified moisture-density tests (AASHO Designation T 180, ASTM Designation D 1557. The Asphalt Institute recommends the use of AASHO Designation T 180, Method D, or ASTM Designation D 1557, Method D, to determine density requirements for subgrades, subbases, and bases. The modification in these methods includes the following (compare with Article 4.15):

   a. Sample—100 percent passing the 3/4-inch sieve
   b. Number of layers in mold—5
   c. Rammer weight—10 pounds
   d. Height of drop of rammer—18 inches
   e. Number of blows per layer—56

4.15 SYNOPSIS OF TEST METHOD

The total sample is permitted to dry in air until a damp condition is reached. From this, a sample of the material passing the No. 4 sieve is selected. The soil is then compacted in three layers into a metal, cylindrical mold of known volume. A metal rammer is dropped from a height of 12 inches onto the soil in the mold. A total of 25 blows per layer is used. The weight of the soil in the mold is determined, and with the volume of the mold known, the density is computed by dividing the weight by the volume. A moisture content determination is made on the sample in the mold. The soil is then removed from the mold, pulverized, an increment of water mixed into the sample, and the compaction procedure repeated. The test continues until the weight of the compacted sample in the mold is equal to or less than that obtained in the preceding step.

4.16 TYPICAL TEST RESULTS

The computations include a plot of the moisture content versus the density obtained with that moisture content. Calculations are then made of the density of the soil grains only, i.e., excluding the weight of the water. This density is also plotted versus the moisture content and is termed the "dry density" curve. The resulting plots are curved lines showing higher densities with increased moisture content up to some peak, and then lower densities with increased moisture content. The density at the peak of the dry-density curve is called the "Maximum Density" and the moisture content at that point is termed the "Optimum Moisture Content."

The following is a list of the range of values that might be anticipated for the standard moisture-density test:

Clays - Maximum density	90-105 lbs. per cu. ft.
Optimum moisture content	20 to 30%
Silty clays - Maximum density	100-115 lbs. per cu.ft.
Optimum moisture content	15 to 25%
Sandy clays - Maximum density	110-135 lbs. per cu. ft.
Optimum moisture content	8 to 15%

For the modified procedure using an increased compactive effort, maximum densities of 10 to 20 pounds per cubic foot larger can be anticipated with optimum moisture contents of 3 to 10% lower.

For sandy or gravelly soils with no fines, there is no significant change in density with the use of water unless inundation methods are used.

Many compaction specifications require that a percent of the maximum density be achieved.* This percent varies from 90 to 95% for the more granular materials and 95 to 100% for the fine-grained silts and clays. The percent of maximum density is the ratio of the density obtained to the maximum density expressed as a percentage.

4.17 INFLUENCES OF THE METHODS OF TEST

The test is not particularly susceptible to dangers from poor laboratory technique. The degree of accuracy of the field density test, and

---

* This sentence should read: This percent varies from 95 to 100% for the more granular materials and 90 to 95% for the fine-grained silts and clays. The percent of maximum density is the ratio of the density obtained to the maximum density expressed as a percentage.

the differences in the soils in the field and that used in the laboratory preclude a highly accurate determination.

However, certain laboratory precautions must be taken. In the mixing of the water into the soil, as thorough a mix as possible is necessary. In taking the moisture sample, care should be taken to obtain a representative sample. For very granular soils with a large portion retained on the No. 4 sieve, an adjustment is necessary to compensate for the removal of this material prior to testing.

There is considerable argument as to the adequacy of the laboratory compaction as compared to that obtained by construction equipment. The question arises as to the size, weight and drop of the rammer, as well as the manner in which the soil is compacted. However, as long as the specifications require the standard test, the argument is not a factor to the construction forces in their routine operations.

The field density test to determine the density obtained by the construction equipment has been successfully conducted using any one of three different devices for measuring the volume of the hole from which a sample has been removed. The three techniques include calibrated sand, a viscous liquid, and water encased in a light rubber membrane. A fourth method involving the removal of a sample by driving a thin-walled sampler into the soil is satisfactory for fine-grained silts and clays but not for material containing a significant amount of gravel or rock fragments.

Chapter V

AMERICAN ASSOCIATION OF STATE HIGHWAY OFFICIALS

CLASSIFICATION SYSTEM FOR SOILS*

A. General

5.01 DEVELOPMENT

The American Association of State Highway Officials (AASHO) system of soil classification is based upon the observed field performance of soils under highway pavements and is widely known and used among highway engineers. The original system was developed by the U. S. Bureau of Public Roads about 1928 and has been revised several times. The most recent revision by the Bureau of Public Roads was published in 1942 and separated highway soils into eight groups. Another extensive revision was made by a committee of highway engineers for the Highway Research Board in 1945. This 1945 version forms the basis for the present AASHO system.

According to this system, soils having approximately the same general load-carrying capacity and service characteristics are grouped together to form seven basic groups which are designated as A-1, A-2, A-3, A-4, A-5, A-6 and A-7, as shown in Table V-1. In general the best soils for highway subgrades are classified as A-1, the next best A-2 and so on with the poorest rating of soils for subgrades being those in the A-7 group. Thus, it may be assumed generally that structural thickness requirements of the pavement progressively increase as the soil classification group increases from A-1 to A-7.

---

* AASHO Designation: M 145.

Table V-1—Classification of Soils and Soil-Aggregate Mixtures

General Classification	Granular Materials (35% or less passing No. 200)			Silt-Clay Materials (More than 35% passing No. 200)			
Group Classification	A-1	A-3*	A-2	A-4	A-5	A-6	A-7
Sieve Analysis Percent passing: No. 10 No. 40 No. 200	50 Max. 25 Max.	51 Min. 10 Max.	35 Max.	36 Min.	36 Min.	36 Min.	36 Min.
Characteristics of Fraction passing No. 40 Liquid limit Plasticity Index	6 Max.	N.P.	—	40 Max. 10 Max.	41 Min. 10 Max.	40 Max. 11 Min.	41 Min. 11 Min.
Group Index	0	0	4 Max.	8 Max.	12 Max.	16 Max.	20 Max.
General Rating as Subgrade	Excellent to Good			Fair to Poor			

* The placing of A-3 before A-2 is necessary in the "left to right elimination process" and does not indicate superiority of A-3 over A-2.

The revised system currently in use employs the seven basic groups previously mentioned and has been subdivided further into twelve subgroups as shown in Table V-2. A group index is used not to place a soil in a specified group, but as a means of evaluating soils as subgrade materials within their groups. The group index is a function of the liquid limit, plasticity index and the amount of material passing the No. 200 sieve. Charts for determining the group index are presented as Figure V-1.

B. Test Procedures

5.02 GENERAL

The classification of a specific soil is based upon the results of tests made in accordance with standard methods of soil testing.

5.03 TEST PROCEDURES

The test procedures to be utilized are either the standard methods of the AASHO or ASTM. The AASHO

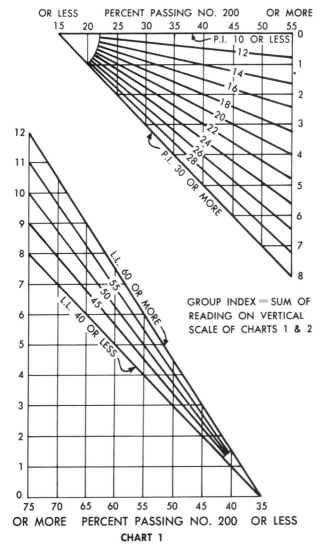

Figure V-1—Group Index Charts.

Table V-2—Classification of Soils and Soil-Aggregate Mixtures (with Suggested Subgroups)

General Classification	Granular Materials (35% or less passing No. 200)							Silt-Clay Materials (More than 35% passing No. 200)			
	A-1		A-3	A-2				A-4	A-5	A-6	A-7
Group Classification	A-1-a	A-1-b		A-2-4	A-2-5	A-2-6	A-2-7				A-7-5; A-7-6
Sieve Analysis: Percent passing:											
No. 10	50 Max.										
No. 40	30 Max.	50 Max.	51 Min.								
No. 200	15 Max.	25 Max.	10 Max.	35 Max.	35 Max.	35 Max.	35 Max.	36 Min.	36 Min.	36 Min.	36 Min.
Characteristics of fraction passing No. 40:											
Liquid Limit				40 Max.	41 Min.	40 Max.	41 Min.	40 Max.	41 Min.	40 Max.	41 Min.
Plasticity Index	6 Max.		N.P.	10 Max.	10 Max.	11 Min.	11 Min.	10 Max.	10 Max.	11 Min.	11 Min.
Group Index	0		0	0	0	4 Max.		8 Max.	12 Max.	16 Max.	20 Max.
Usual Types of Significant Constituent Materials	Stone Fragments Gravel and Sand		Fine Sand	Silty or Clayey Gravel and Sand				Silty Soils		Clayey Soils	
General Rating as Subgrade	Excellent to Good							Fair to Poor			

Plasticity index of A-7-5 subgroup is equal to or less than LL minus 30. Plasticity index of A-7-6 subgroup is greater than LL minus 30 (see figure V-2). Group index should be indicated to the nearest whole number in parentheses after group symbol (A-2-6[3], A-4[5], etc.). Classification Procedure: With the required test data, proceed from left to right on above chart, and correct group will be found by the process of elimination. The first group from left into which the test data will fit is the correct classification.

— 58 —

test procedures are described in detail in Appendix A, and the ASTM standard procedures may be found in the *ASTM Standards, 1961*, Part 4. A listing of the corresponding AASHO and ASTM designations to be utilized follows:

Standard Tests	Designation	
	AASHO	ASTM
a. Sieve Analysis of Fine and Coarse Aggregate	T 27	C 136
b. Mechanical Analysis of Soils	T 88	D 422
c. Liquid Limit of Soils	T 89	D 423
d. Plastic Limit of Soils	T 90	D 424
e. Calculating the Plasticity Index	T 91	D 424

C. Classification

5.04 GENERAL

After the necessary laboratory tests have been performed, the proper classification for a given material can normally be made without great difficulty. Nevertheless, the individual making the classification should be aware of several terms which frequently arise in connection with this classification system. Moreover, an understanding of certain peculiarities and general performance characteristics of the various soil types is essential to their proper use as highway materials. For this reason, a more detailed discussion of the frequently occurring terms and the various soil groups is included.

5.05 SOIL FRACTIONS

According to the AASHO system, soils are divided into two major groups as shown in Table V-2. These are the granular materials with 35 percent or less passing the No. 200 sieve and the silt-clay materials with more than 35 percent passing the No. 200 sieve. Moreover, five soil fractions are recognized and often used in word descriptions of a material. These five fractions are defined as follows:

a. *Boulders*—material retained on 3-inch sieve. They should be excluded from the portion of a sample to which the classification is applied, but the percentage of such material should be recorded.

b. *Gravel*—material passing sieve with 3-inch square openings and retained on the No. 10 sieve.

c. *Coarse sand*—material passing the No. 10 sieve and retained on the No. 40 sieve.

d. *Fine sand*—material passing the No. 40 sieve and retained on the No. 200 sieve.

e. *Combined silt and clay*—material passing the No. 200 sieve. The word "silty" is applied to a fine material having a plasticity index of 10 or less, and the term "clayey" is applied to fine material having a P. I. of more than 10.

5.06 DESCRIPTION OF CLASSIFICATION GROUPS

The two major groups in the soil classification are further divided into additional groups and subgroups as follows:

a. Granular materials:

Group A-1—Well-graded mixtures of stone fragments or gravel ranging from coarse to fine with a nonplastic or slightly plastic soil binder. However, this group also includes coarse materials without soil binder.

Subgroup A-1-a—Materials consisting predominantly of stone fragments or gravel, either with or without a well-graded soil binder.

Subgroup A-1-b—Materials consisting predominantly of coarse sand either with or without a well-graded soil binder.

Group A-3—Materials consisting of sands deficient in coarse material and soil binder. Typical is fine beach sand or fine desert blow sand, without silt or clay fines or with a very small amount of nonplastic silt. This group also includes stream-deposited mixtures of poorly graded fine sand and limited amounts of coarse sand and gravel. These soils make suitable subgrades for all types of pavements when confined and damp. They are subject to erosion and have been known to pump and blow under rigid pavements. They can be compacted by vibratory, pneumatic-tired, and steel-wheel rollers but not with a sheepsfoot roller.

Group A-2—This group includes a wide variety of "granular" materials which are borderline between the materials falling in Groups A-1 and A-3 and the silt-clay materials of Groups A-4, A-5, A-6, and A-7. It includes all materials containing 35 percent or less passing the No. 200 sieve which cannot be classified as A-1 or A-3.

> Subgroups A-2-4 and A-2-5 include various granular materials containing 35 percent or less passing the No. 200 sieve, and with that portion passing No. 40 sieve having the characteristics of the A-4 and A-5 groups. These groups include such materials as gravel and coarse sand with silt contents or plasticity indexes in excess of the limitations of Group A-1, and fine sand with nonplastic silt content in excess of the limitations of Group A-3.

> Subgroups A-2-6 and A-2-7 include materials similar to those described under Subgroups A-2-4 and A-2-5, except that the fine portion contains plastic clay having the characteristics of the A-6 or A-7 group. The approximate combined effects of plasticity indexes in excess of 10 and percentages passing the No. 200 sieve in excess of 15 is reflected by group index values of 0 to 4.

A-2 soils are given a poorer rating than A-1 soils because of inferior binder, poor grading, or a combination of the two. Depending on the character and amount of binder, A-2 soils may become soft during wet weather and loose and dusty in dry weather when used as a road surface. If, however, they are protected from these extreme changes in moisture content, they may be quite stable. The A-2-4 and A-2-5 soils are satisfactory as base materials when properly compacted and drained, while A-2-6 and A-2-7 soils may lose stability because of capillary saturation or lack of drainage. A-2-6 and A-2-7 soils with low percentages of minus 200 material are classified as good bases, whereas these same soils with high percentages of minus 200 and P. I.'s of 10 or higher are questionable as a base material. Frequently the A-2 soils are employed as a cover material for very plastic subgrades.

b. *Silt-Clay Materials:*

Group A-4—The typical material of this group is a nonplastic or moderately plastic silty soil usually having 75 percent or more passing the No. 200 sieve. The group includes also mixtures of fine silty soil and up to 64 percent of sand and gravel retained on the No. 200 sieve. The group index values range from 1 to 8, with increasing percentages of coarse material being reflected by decreasing group index values. These predominantly silty soils are quite common in occurrence. Their texture varies from sandy loams to silty and clayey loams. With the proper amount of moisture present, they may perform well as a pavement component. However, they frequently have an affinity for water and will swell and lose much of their stability unless properly compacted and drained. Moreover, they are subject to frost heave. Since these soils do not drain readily and may absorb water by capillarity with resulting loss in strength, the pavement structural design section should be based on the strength of the soils when saturated. The silty loams are often difficult to compact properly. Careful field control of moisture content and pneumatic-tired rollers are normally required for proper compaction.

Group A-5—The typical material of this group is similar to that described under Group A-4, except that it is usually of diatomaceous or micaceous character and may be highly elastic as indicated by the high liquid limit. The group index values. range from 1 to 12, with increasing values indicating the combined effect of increasing liquid limits and decreasing percentages of coarse material. These soils do not occur as widely as the A-4 soils. They are normally elastic or resilient in both the damp and semi-dry conditions. They are subject to frost heave, erosion, and loss of stability if not properly drained. Since these soils do not drain readily and may absorb water by capillarity with resulting loss in strength, the pavement structural design section should be based on the strength of the soils when saturated. Careful control of moisture content is normally required for proper compaction.

Group A-6—The typical material of this group is a plastic clay soil usually having 75 percent or more passing the No. 200 sieve. The group includes also mixtures of fine clayey soil and up to 64 percent of sand and gravel retained on the No. 200 sieve. Materials of this group usually have high volume change between wet and dry states. The group index values range from 1 to 16, with increasing values indicating the combined effect of increasing plasticity indexes and decreasing percentages of coarse material. These soils are quite common in occurrence and are widely used in fills. When moisture content is properly controlled, they compact quite readily with either a sheepsfoot or pneumatic-tired roller. They have high dry strength but lose much of this strength upon absorbing water. The A-6 soils will compress when wet and shrink and swell with changes in moisture content. When placed in the shoulders adjacent to the pavement, they tend to shrink away from the pavement edge upon drying and thereby provide an access route to the underside of the pavement for surface water. The A-6 soils do not drain readily and may absorb water by capillarity with resulting loss in strength. Therefore, the pavement

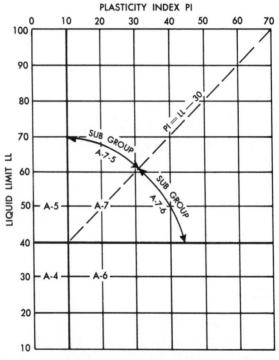

Figure V-2—Liquid Limit and Plasticity Index Ranges for the A-4, A-5, A-6 and A-7 Subgroups.

structural design section should be based on the strength of the soils when saturated.

Group A-7—The typical materials and problems of this group are similar to those described under Group A-6, except that they have the high liquid limits characteristic of the A-5 group and may be elastic as well as subject to high volume change. The range of group index values is 1 to 20, with increasing values indicating the combined effect of increasing liquid limits and plasticity indexes and decreasing percentages of coarse material.

Subgroup A-7-5—includes those materials with moderate plasticity indexes in relation to liquid limit and which may be highly elastic as well as subject to considerable volume change.

Subgroup A-7-6—includes those materials with high plasticity indexes in relation to liquid limit and which are subject to extremely high volume change.

Highly organic soils such as peat and muck are not included in this classification. Because of their many undesirable properties, their use should be avoided, if possible, in all types of construction.

5.07 AASHO CLASSIFICATION PROCEDURE

The final soil classification is obtained by using the results obtained from the required tests of Section B and Appendix A in Table V-1 or, if a more detailed classification is desired, by using Table V-2 and Figure V-2. Using the test data, proceed from left to right in Table V-1 or Table V-2, and the correct group will be found by process of elimination. The first group from the left into which the test data will fit is the correct classification. All limiting test values are shown as whole numbers. If fractional numbers appear on test reports, convert to nearest whole number for purposes of classification. Group index values should always be shown in parentheses after group symbol as: A-2-6(3), A-4(5), A-6(12), and A-7-5(17). Suggested forms for recording test and reporting test data are included in Appendix A.

Chapter VI

UNIFIED SOIL CLASSIFICATION SYSTEM

A. General

6.01 DEVELOPMENT

Professor Arthur Casagrande proposed the soil classification system that is now called the *Unified System* as a means of classifying soils in accordance with their value as subgrades for roads and airfields. His work in this field convinced him that textural classification was inadequate for cohesive soils. He found that cohesive soils could be grouped in accordance with their position on a plot of plasticity index versus liquid limit. By the early 1940's sufficient data had been collected to formulate the Unified System, and it was adopted by the Corps of Engineers for airfield work in 1942. In 1947 the Corps incorporated certain arbitrary limits to prevent dual classification. Other agencies also had been using the system, and both the Corps and the Bureau of Reclamation extended its usage to all phases of soils work. Discussion in 1952 between the Corps and the Bureau, with Dr. Casagrande acting as a consultant, resulted in an agreement on a modification of the Airfield Classification System which was named the *Unified Soil Classification System*.

This chapter will present information as contained in "The Unified Soil Classification System," Corps of Engineers, U. S. Army, *Technical Memorandum No. 3-357*, Vols. 1 and 3, March 1953.

6.02 BASIS OF THE UNIFIED SYSTEM

The Unified Soil Classification System is based on textural characteristics for those soils with such a small amount of fines that the fines do not affect the behavior.

It is based on plasticity-compressibility characteristics for those soils where the fines affect the behavior. The plasticity-compressibility characteristics are evaluated by plotting the plasticity index versus the liquid limit on a standard plasticity chart. The position of the plotted points yields information from which to predict behavior as an engineering construction material. The following properties form the basis of soil identification:

a. Percentages of gravel, sand and fines (fraction passing No. 200 sieve).

b. Shape of the grain-size-distribution curve.

c. Plasticity and compressibility characteristics.

A soil is given a descriptive name and letter symbol to indicate its principal characteristics.

6.03 DEFINITIONS OF SOIL FRACTIONS

Four soil fractions are recognized in this system to designate the size ranges of soil fractions. These four fractions are "cobbles," "gravel," "sand," and "fines," and the limiting textural boundaries for these have been arbitrarily set as indicated in the following tabulation:

Component	Size Range
Cobbles	Above 3 in.
Gravel	3 in. to No. 4 sieve
Coarse gravel	3 in. to ¾ in.
Fine gravel	¾ in. to No. 4 sieve
Sand	No. 4 to No. 200
Coarse	No. 4 to No. 10
Medium	No. 10 to No. 40
Fine	No. 40 to No. 200
Fines (silt or clay)	Below No. 200 sieve

The minus No. 200 sieve material is "silt" if nonplastic and the liquid limit and plasticity index plot below the "A" line on the plasticity chart (Figure VI-1); and "clay" if plastic and the liquid limit and plasticity index plot above the "A" line. This holds true for inorganic

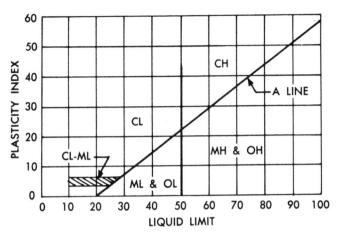

Figure VI-1—Plasticity Chart.

silts and clays and organic silts, but not for organic clays, since they plot below the "A" line. The "A" line is an arbitrarily drawn line on the Plasticity Chart of Figure VI-1 and, as Dr. Casagrande discovered, generally separates the more clay-like materials from those that are silt-like.

B. Soil Groups

6.04 GENERAL

This system places soils into three divisions: (1) coarse-grained, (2) fine-grained, and (3) highly organic soils. The coarse-grained soils are those having 50 percent or less material passing the No. 200 sieve, and fine-grained soils are those having more than 50 percent passing the No. 200 sieve. The highly organic soils can generally be identified by visual examination. This system recognizes 15 soil groups and uses names and letter symbols to distinguish between these groups. These letter symbols are easily remembered. They are derived either from the terms descriptive of the soil fractions, the relative value of the liquid limit (high or low), or relative gradation (well-graded or poorly graded). The symbols are as follows:

Components and Corresponding Symbols

Boulders—None	Silt—M
Cobbles—None	Clay—C
Gravel—G	Organic—O
Sand—S	Peat—Pt

Gradation Symbols	*Liquid Limit Symbols*
Well-graded—W	High L. L.—H
Poorly graded—P	Low L. L.—L

These symbols are combined to form the group symbols which correspond to the names of typical soils as seen in Table VI-1. These symbols are also used in combination in describing borderline soils.

6.05 COARSE-GRAINED SOILS

The coarse-grained soils are subdivided into gravels and gravelly soils (G), and sands and sandy soils (S). The gravels are those having the greater percentage of the coarse fraction (particles larger than 0.074 mm diameter) retained on the No. 4 sieve, and the sands are those having the greater portion passing the No. 4 sieve. Both the gravel (G) and sand (S) groups are divided into four secondary groups as discussed below:

a. GW and SW groups comprise well-graded gravelly soils and sandy soils with little or no nonplastic fines (less than 5 percent passing the No. 200 sieve). The presence of fines must not noticeably change the strength properties of the coarse-grained fraction, and must not interfere with its free-draining characteristics. In areas subject to frost action, the material should not contain more than about 3 percent of soil grains smaller than 0.02 mm in size.

b. GP and SP groups are poorly graded gravels and sands with little or no nonplastic fines. These materials may be classed as uniform gravels, uniform sand, or gap-graded materials.

c. *GM and SM* groups comprise silty (M) gravels and silty sands with fines (more than 12 percent* passing No. 200 sieve) having low or no plasticity. The liquid limit and plasticity index (based on minus No. 40 sieve fraction) should plot below the "A" line on the plasticity chart. Both well-graded and poorly graded materials are included in these two groups. Normally these soils have little to no dry strength, but occasionally the fines or binder material will contain a natural cementing agent which will increase dry strength. The basic soil groups, GM and SM, have each been subdivided into two groups designated by the suffixes *d* and *u* which have been chosen to represent desirable and less desirable (undesirable) base materials, respectively. This subdivision applies to roads and airfields only and is based on field observation and laboratory tests on the behavior of the soils in these groups. Basis for the subdivision is the liquid limit and plasticity index of the fraction of the soil passing the No. 40 sieve. The suffix d is used when the liquid limit is 25 or less and the plasticity index is 5 or less; the suffix u is used otherwise. Typical symbols for soils in these groups are GMd and SMu.

d. *GC and SC* groups comprise gravelly or sandy soils with fines (more than 12 percent passing the No. 200 sieve) that are more clay-like and which range in plasticity from low to high. The liquid limits and plasticity indexes of soils in this group should plot above the "A" line on the plasticity chart. Both well- and poorly graded materials are included in these groups.

---

* Soils having between 5 percent and 12 percent passing the No. 200 sieve are classed as "borderline" and are discussed in Article 6.12k of this chapter.

6.06 FINE-GRAINED SOILS

The fine-grained soils are subdivided into silts (M for the Swedish terms mo and mjala or flour) and clays (C) based on their liquid limit and plasticity index. Moreover, organic soils (O) are also included in this fraction. Silts are those fine-grained soils which have liquid limits and plasticity indexes that plot below the "A" line on the plasticity chart, and clays are those that plot above the "A" line in Figure VI-1. Organic clays are the exception to the above rule, as the liquid limits and plasticity indexes of these soils plot below the "A" line. The silt, clay and organic fractions are further subdivided on the basis of relatively low (L) or high (H) liquid limits. The arbitrary dividing line between the low and high liquid limits has been set at 50. Representative soil types for each of these groups (ML, MH, CL, CH, OL, and OH) can be found in Table VI-1, under the column "Typical Names." Moreover, a brief discussion of these secondary groups of fine-grained silts and clays follows:

a. *ML and MH* groups are soils classed as sandy silts, clayey silts, or inorganic silts with relatively low plasticity. Loess-type soils, rock flours, micaceous and diatomaceous soils are also included. Some types of kaolin clays and illite clays also fall within these groups.

b. *CH and CL* groups are primarily inorganic clays. The CH groups, medium and high plasticity clays, include the fat clays, gumbo clays, bentonite, and certain volcanic clays. The low plasticity clays are classified CL and are usually lean clays, sandy clays, or silty clays. The glacial clays of the northern United States cover a wide band in these two groups.

c. *OL and OH* groups are soils characterized by the presence of organic matter. Organic silts and clays are classified in these two groups, and they have a plasticity range corresponding to the ML and MH groups.

6.07 HIGHLY ORGANIC SOILS

These soils are not subdivided but classified into one group (Pt). They are usually very compressible and have undesirable construction characteristics. Typical soils of this group are peat, humus, and swamp soils with a highly organic texture. Common components of these soils are particles of leaves, grass, branches, or other fibrous vegetable matter.

6.08 CHARACTERISTICS PERTINENT TO ROADS AND AIRFIELDS

Additional general characteristics of the fifteen soil groups discussed in Articles 6.05, 6.06, and 6.07, which are pertinent to roads and airfields, are summarized in Table VI-2. General characteristics of the soil groups pertinent to foundations and embankments may be found in Appendix A, Vol. 2, *The Unified Soil Classification System*, Corps of Engineers, U. S. Army, TM No. 3-357, March, 1953.

C. Field Classification

6.09 GENERAL

This system is so designed that most soils may be classified into, at least, the three primary groups (coarse-grained, fine-grained, and highly organic) by means of visual inspection and simple field tests. Moreover, with experience, classification into the subdivisions can also be made by visual inspection with a considerable degree of success. Since most soils are given, at least, a preliminary classification in the field, the ability to field classify by means of the unified system is a great advantage. When required, a more positive identification may be made by means of laboratory tests on the materials. The field and laboratory methods of identification are discussed separately in this chapter, even though they are similar in many respects. With practice, it is possible for one to become quite proficient in field classification of soils.

6.10 EQUIPMENT

This field classification procedure has the great advantage of not requiring any special equipment. However, the following items will facilitate the work:

a. Rubber syringe or small oil can.

b. Supply of clear water.

c. Small bottle of dilute hydrochloric acid.

d. Familiarity with the descriptive information found in Table VI-1.

e. U. S. standard sieves (No. 4 and 200).

6.11 TEST PROCEDURES

The tests utilized in field identification are the dilatancy or shake test, dry strength, and toughness or consistency near the plastic limit. Procedures for performing these simple tests may be found in the first column to the right of Table VI-1.

6.12 CLASSIFICATION PROCEDURE

The field classification procedure is listed below and consists of a process of elimination, beginning at the left side of Table VI-1 and working to the right until the proper group name is obtained. Moreover, all pertinent descriptive information should be noted while performing these steps.

a. Obtain a representative sample of the soil.

b. Estimate the size of the largest particle.

c. Remove the boulders and cobbles, particles larger than 3 inches, and estimate the amount, percentage by weight, in the total sample.

d. Spread the dry sample on a flat surface or in the palm of the hand, and classify as coarse-grained or fine-grained. Individual grains of a coarse-grained soil can be distinguished with the unaided eye, whereas the individual grains of the fine fraction cannot.

e. If coarse-grained, classify as gravel or sand by criteria shown on the table.

f. If gravel or sand, classify as "clean" or "with appreciable fines." Fines are the fraction smaller than 0.074 mm (No. 200 sieve).

g. If the gravel or sand is clean, decide if it is well-graded (W) or poorly graded (P), and assign the appropriate group name (GW, GP, SW, or SP).

h. If the gravel or sand contains appreciable fines, decide if the fines are silty (M) or clayey (C), and classify as GM, GC, SM, or SC. The "teeth test" is sometimes used for this purpose by biting a piece of the sample; the clay tends to stick to the teeth, while the silt does not. Also fine sand may be distinguished from silt and clay by rubbing a small amount between the fingers. Silt or clay feels smooth and will leave a stain, whereas fine sand feels gritty and will not stain the fingers.

i. For fine-grained soils or the fine-grained portion of a coarse-grained soil, the dilatancy, dry strength, and toughness tests are performed in accordance with instructions given in the table. In addition, observations of color and odor are important, particularly for organic soils (OL and OH groups are drab shades of gray, brown, or almost black and have a distinctive odor). Through the process of elimination and use of the field test results, these soils are then given the proper group symbol and descriptive identification.

j. Highly organic soils (Pt) are characterized by undecayed particles of leaves, sticks, grass, and other vegetable matter giving the soil a fibrous texture. They are spongy, dull brown to black in color, and have a characteristic odor. Low-lying, swampy areas usually contain highly organic soils.

k. Soils which have characteristics of two groups are given boundary classification using a name most nearly describing the soil, and the two group symbols are such as GW-GC. Boundary classifications which are common are: Coarse-grained gravelly soils—GW-GC, GW-GM, GW-GP, GM-GC, and similarly for sand; for fine-grained soils—ML-MH, CL-CH, OL-OH, CL-ML, ML-OL, CL-OL, MH-CH, MH-OH, and CH-OH soils; and for boundary classifications between coarse and fine-grained soils—SM-ML and SC-CL.

D. Laboratory Classification

6.13 GENERAL

The same descriptive information as required for field classification is also necessary for the laboratory classification. The field classification is checked and refined by employing common items of laboratory equipment to perform simple and routine tests such as gradation, liquid limit, and plastic limit. The gradation is determined by sieve analysis, and a grain-size curve is usually plotted as percent finer (or passing) by weight against a log scale of grain size in millimeters. Figure VI-2 shows examples of typical grain-size distribution curves. Plasticity characteristics are evaluated using the liquid limit and plastic limit tests on the soil fraction finer than the No. 40 sieve. The criteria for classifying soils are given in column 7 of Table VI-1. The plasticity chart is used to classify the fine-grained soils and the fine-grained portion of coarse-grained soils.

6.14 TEST PROCEDURES

The test procedures used are either the standard methods of the AASHO or ASTM. The AASHO test procedures and necessary equipment are described in detail in Appendix A, and the ASTM standard procedures and a description of necessary equipment are in the *ASTM Standards, 1961*, Part 4. A listing of the corresponding AASHO and ASTM test designations to be utilized follows:

Standard Tests	Designation	
	AASHO	ASTM
a. Sieve Analysis of Fine and Coarse Aggregate	T 27	C 136
b. Specific Gravity of Soil	T 100	D 854
c. Mechanical Analysis of Soils	T 88	D 422
d. Liquid Limit of Soils	T 89*	D 423*
e. Plastic Limit of Soils	T 90*	D 424*
f. Calculating the Plasticity Index	T 91*	D 424*

*Note: The Corps of Engineers has modified for its use the methods of test for liquid limit and plastic limit of soils as follows:

1. The sample shall not be oven-dried nor subjected to any artificial drying before processing for testing.

2. The sample shall be soaked in water for 24 hours prior to washing.

3. The sample shall be washed through the No. 40 sieve. Material retained on the sieve shall be dried, then dry-sieved through the No. 40 sieve. The portion dry-sieved through the No. 40 sieve shall be combined with the material washed through the sieve. This combination shall be used for the liquid and plastic limit tests.

4. The sample shall be set aside and the water decanted or wicked off. No chemicals shall be added to hasten

settlement of fines. The sample shall be dried to approximately the liquid limit with care being taken to prevent caking or lumping during the drying process. The liquid limit test shall be performed from wet of the liquid limit to dry of the liquid limit, using the mechanical method. No dry soil shall ever be added to the sample during performance of either the liquid limit or plastic limit test.

5. Water content shall be further reduced by air-drying and the plastic limit test performed. Drying shall not proceed below the plastic limit. Care shall be taken to prevent caking or lumping during drying.

6. The plastic limit test shall be performed on a ground glass plate.

7. Modifications to the soaking time and to the method of hastening settlement of the fines will be made when check tests of the specification material show that the modifications do not affect results.

6.15 CLASSIFICATION PROCEDURE

The procedure for the laboratory classification is presented in Table VI-3, and briefly enumerated below:

a. Determine if the soil is coarse-grained, fine-grained, or highly organic. This may be accomplished by visual inspection or by determining the amount of soil passing the No. 200 sieve.

b. If coarse-grained: (1) Perform a sieve analysis and plot gradation curve on a grain-size chart. Determine percentage passing the No. 4 sieve and classify as gravel (greater percentage retained on No. 4) or sand (greater percentage passes No. 4).

(2) Determine amount of material passing the No. 200 sieve. If less than 5 percent passes the No. 200 sieve and the fine fraction does not interfere with the soil's free-draining properties, examine shape of the grain-size curve, and if well-graded, classify as

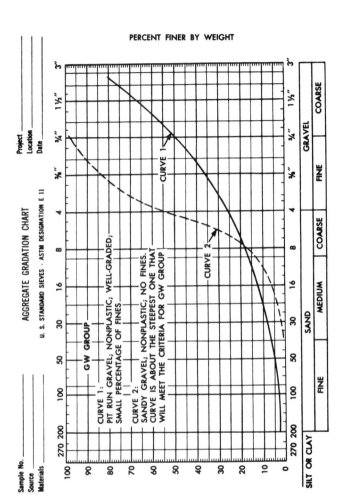

Figure VI-2(a)—Typical Example of GW Soil

— 79 —

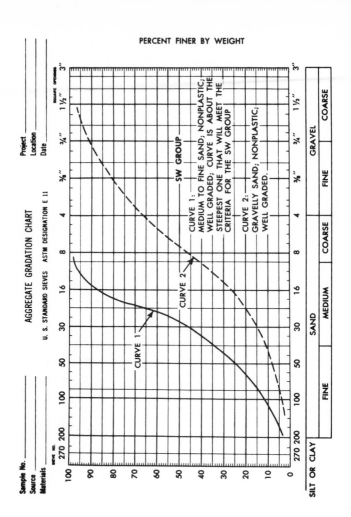

Figure VI-2(b)—Typical Example of SW Soil

GW or SW; if poorly-graded, as GP or SP. If fines interfere with free-draining properties, use double symbol, such as GW-GM.

(3) If between 5 percent and 12 percent of the material passes the No. 200 sieve, it is a borderline case, and the classification should have double symbol appropriate to grading and plasticity characteristics (GW-GM, SW-SM, etc.).

(4) If more than 12 percent passes the No. 200 sieve, perform the liquid limit and plastic limit tests on the minus No. 40 sieve fraction. Use the plasticity chart to determine the correct classification (GM, SM, GC, SC, GM-GC, or SM-SC).

c. If *fine-grained*: (1) Perform liquid limit and plastic limit tests on minus No. 40 sieve material. If the liquid limit is less than 50, classify as "L" and if the liquid limit is greater than 50, classify as "H."

(2) For "L": if limits plot *below* "A" line and the hatched zone on the plasticity chart, determine by color, odor, or the change in liquid limit and plastic limit caused by oven-drying the soil, whether it is organic (OL) or inorganic (ML). If the limits plot *in* the hatched zone, classify as ML-CL. If the limits plot *above* the "A" line and the hatched zone on the plasticity chart, classify as CL.

(3) For "H": if the limits plot below the "A" line on the plasticity chart, determine whether organic (OH) or inorganic (MH). If the limits plot above the "A" line, classify as CH.

d. A detailed discussion of the borderline classifications of this system is not deemed essential in this discussion, since the majority of thickness design charts do not actually consider these. However, a more detailed discussion can be found in Technical Memorandum No. 3-357, *The Unified Soil Classification System*, Vol. 1, Corps of Engineers, 1953.

6.16 THE USE OF DESCRIPTIVE TERMS TO CLASSIFY A SOIL FURTHER

Although the use of letter symbols is convenient, and has been stressed in this chapter, it does not describe a soil as completely as is normally required. For this reason, descriptive terms should be used and arranged in sentence form in addition to the letter symbols to produce a more complete soil classification.

In the case of all soils, such things as color, odor, and homogeneity of deposit should be observed and included in the description.

For coarse-grained soils such items as grain shape, mineralogical content, degree of weathering, degree of compaction, and presence or absence of fines should be noted and included. Commonly used adjectives such as rounded, angular, and subangular are employed to describe grain shape. The degree of compaction is normally obtained by observing the ease or difficulty encountered in excavating the material, or in penetrating it with devices designed for this purpose. Such terms as very loose, loose, medium, dense, and very dense are frequently used. A granular deposit which can, for example, be excavated readily with the hands would be considered very loose, whereas a deposit of the same material which requires power tools for excavation would be classed as very dense.

For the fine-grained fraction, such items as natural water content and consistency and remolded consistency should be noted in the word description. Consistency in the natural state corresponds in some respects to degree of compaction in coarse-grained soils and is usually evaluated by noting the ease by which the deposit can be excavated or penetrated. Such terms as very soft, soft, medium, and hard are employed to describe consistency. Most textbooks on soil mechanics include tables or rules of thumb for determining and describing both the consistency of fine-grained soil and the degree of compaction of granular deposits.

In addition to the descriptive terms discussed above, it is normally considered wise and desirable to include the geological and pedological (agricultural) classification with the word description if this information is available or can be readily obtained. Such terms as old glacial lake-bed material or Miami silt-loam may be quite helpful to any person who is familiar with these terms and the soil types they normally represent.

6.17 ENGINEERING USE CHART. The investigator of earth foundations or borrow materials often likes to compare the soil he has classified with other kinds of foundation or construction materials. The Bureau of Reclamation, United States Department of the Interior, has prepared an engineering use chart, Figure VI-3, to provide this information.

The chart compares the desirability of the different soil groups for use in rolled earth dams, canal sections, foundations, and roadways. The numerical ratings given in the chart are approximate only. They are intended as a guide to aid the investigator in comparing soils for various purposes.

TYPICAL NAMES OF SOIL GROUPS	GROUP SYMBOLS	IMPORTANT PROPERTIES			
		PERMEABILITY WHEN COMPACTED	SHEARING STRENGTH WHEN COMPACTED AND SATURATED	COMPRESSIBILITY WHEN COMPACTED AND SATURATED	WORKABILITY AS A CONSTRUCTION MATERIAL
WELL-GRADED GRAVELS, GRAVEL-SAND MIXTURES, LITTLE OR NO FINES.	GW	PERVIOUS	EXCELLENT	NEGLIGIBLE	EXCELLENT
POORLY GRADED GRAVELS, GRAVEL-SAND MIXTURES, LITTLE OR NO FINES.	GP	VERY PERVIOUS	GOOD	NEGLIGIBLE	GOOD
SILTY GRAVELS, POORLY GRADED GRAVEL-SAND-SILT MIXTURES.	GM	SEMIPERVIOUS TO IMPERVIOUS	GOOD	NEGLIGIBLE	GOOD
CLAYEY GRAVELS, POORLY GRADED GRAVEL-SAND-CLAY MIXTURES.	GC	IMPERVIOUS	GOOD TO FAIR	VERY LOW	GOOD
WELL-GRADED SANDS, GRAVELLY SANDS, LITTLE OR NO FINES.	SW	PERVIOUS	EXCELLENT	NEGLIGIBLE	EXCELLENT
POORLY GRADED SANDS, GRAVELLY SANDS, LITTLE OR NO FINES.	SP	PERVIOUS	GOOD	VERY LOW	FAIR
SILTY SANDS, POORLY GRADED SAND-SILT MIXTURES.	SM	SEMIPERVIOUS TO IMPERVIOUS	GOOD	LOW	FAIR
CLAYEY SANDS, POORLY GRADED SAND-CLAY MIXTURES.	SC	IMPERVIOUS	GOOD TO FAIR	LOW	GOOD
INORGANIC SILTS AND VERY FINE SANDS, ROCK FLOUR, SILTY OR CLAYEY FINE SANDS WITH SLIGHT PLASTICITY.	ML	SEMIPERVIOUS TO IMPERVIOUS	FAIR	MEDIUM	FAIR
INORGANIC CLAYS OF LOW TO MEDIUM PLASTICITY, GRAVELLY CLAYS, SANDY CLAYS, SILTY CLAYS, LEAN CLAYS.	CL	IMPERVIOUS	FAIR	MEDIUM	GOOD TO FAIR
ORGANIC SILTS AND ORGANIC SILT-CLAYS OF LOW PLASTICITY.	OL	SEMIPERVIOUS TO IMPERVIOUS	POOR	MEDIUM	FAIR
INORGANIC SILTS, MICACEOUS OR DIATOMACEOUS FINE SANDY OR SILTY SOILS, ELASTIC SILTS.	MH	SEMIPERVIOUS TO IMPERVIOUS	FAIR TO POOR	HIGH	POOR
INORGANIC CLAYS OF HIGH PLASTICITY, FAT CLAYS.	CH	IMPERVIOUS	POOR	HIGH	POOR
ORGANIC CLAYS OF MEDIUM TO HIGH PLASTICITY.	OH	IMPERVIOUS	POOR	HIGH	POOR
PEAT AND OTHER HIGHLY ORGANIC SOILS.	PT	——	——	——	——

* NOTE: NO.1 IS THE BEST

Figure VI-3—Engineering Use Chart.

RELATIVE DESIRABILITY FOR VARIOUS USES *

ROLLED EARTH DAMS			CANAL SECTIONS		FOUNDATIONS		ROADWAYS		
							FILLS		
HOMO-GENEOUS EMBANK-MENT	CORE	SHELL	EROSION RESISTANCE	COMPACTED EARTH LINING	SEEPAGE IMPORTANT	SEEPAGE NOT IMPORTANT	FROST HEAVE NOT POSSIBLE	FROST HEAVE POSSIBLE	SURFACING
—	—	1	1	—	—	1	1	1	3
—	—	2	2	—	—	3	3	3	—
2	4	—	4	4	1	4	4	9	5
1	1	—	3	1	2	6	5	5	1
—	—	3 IF GRAVELLY	6	—	—	2	2	2	4
—	—	4 IF GRAVELLY	7 IF GRAVELLY	—	—	5	6	4	—
4	5	—	8 IF GRAVELLY	5 EROSION CRITICAL	3	7	8	10	6
3	2	—	5	2	4	8	7	6	2
6	6	—	—	6 EROSION CRITICAL	6	9	10	11	—
5	3	—	9	3	5	10	9	7	7
8	8	—	—	7 EROSION CRITICAL	7	11	11	12	—
9	9	—	—	—	8	12	12	13	—
7	7	—	10	8 VOLUME CHANGE CRITICAL	9	13	13	8	—
10	10	—	—	—	10	14	14	14	—
—	—	—	—	—	—	—	—	—	—

(Courtesy—Bureau of Reclamation, U.S. Department of the Interior)

Chapter VII

FEDERAL AVIATION AGENCY METHOD
OF SOIL AND SUBGRADE CLASSIFICATION

A. General

7.01 DEVELOPMENT AND DESCRIPTION

This engineering soil classification system was established in 1944 by the Civil Aeronautics Administration (now Federal Aviation Agency) for classifying soils in the order of their value as subgrade for airfield pavements. This original classification divided soils into ten groups, designated by the symbols E-1 through E-10, decreasing in value as subgrade materials from E-1 through E-10. In 1946, the CAA published a new edition which introduced a number of subdivisions into the system and also altered the test limits of some for the groups. Since 1946 other revisions have been made and the system as presented in this chapter is essentially identical to that described in *Airport Paving*, published by the Federal Aviation Agency, U. S. Department of Commerce, in November, 1962.

The FAA soil classification basically requires the performance of three soil tests: the mechanical analysis, and the determination of the liquid limit and plastic limit (plasticity index). These test results are used to determine the soil group into which a soil will fall. Currently thirteen groups—E-1 through E-13—are recognized. The soil groups of this system are shown in Table VII-1 and will be discussed in more detail subsequently.

The FAA recognizes the fact that a single soil in a given soil group might perform differently as a subgrade material under varying conditions of climate, topography, and drainage. Therefore, for each soil group there are

Table VII-1—Classification of Soils for Airport Pavement Construction

CLASSIFICATION OF SOILS FOR AIRPORT PAVEMENT CONSTRUCTION

Soil group		Material retained on No. 10 sieve—percent [1]	Mechanical analysis			Liquid limit	Plasticity index
			Material finer than No. 10 sieve—percent				
			Coarse sand, passing No. 10; retained on No. 60	Fine sand, passing No. 60; retained on No. 270	Combined silt and clay; passing No. 270		
Granular	E-1	0–45	40+	60–	15–	25–	6–
	E-2	0–45	15+	85–	25–	25–	6–
	E-3	0–45	------	------	25–	25–	6–
	E-4	0–45	------	------	35–	35–	10–
	E-5	0–45	------	------	45–	40–	15–
Fine grained	E-6	0–55	------	------	45+	40–	10–
	E-7	0–55	------	------	45+	50–	10–30
	E-8	0–55	------	------	45+	60–	15–40
	E-9	0–55	------	------	45+	40+	30–
	E-10	0–55	------	------	45+	70–	20–50
	E-11	0–55	------	------	45+	80–	30+
	E-12	0–55	------	------	45+	80+	------
	E-13	Muck and peat—field examination					

[1] If percentage of material retained on the No. 10 sieve exceeds that shown, the classification may be raised, provided such material is sound and fairly well graded.

Federal Aviation Agency

corresponding subgrade classes based upon the performance of the particular soil as a subgrade material for flexible pavements under different conditions of drainage and frost. The subgrade class is determined by soil tests and information obtained from soil and pavement surveys combined with climatological and topographic data. The subgrade classes for flexible pavements and their relationship to the soil groups are shown in Table VII-2.

B. Test Procedures

7.02 GENERAL

The classification of a specific soil into a soil group is based on the results of the three tests as previously mentioned. These tests should be performed in accordance with standard methods of soil testing.

7.03 TEST PROCEDURES

The test procedures are the standard methods of either AASHO or ASTM. The AASHO test procedures are described in detail in Appendix A, and the ASTM standard procedures may be found in the *ASTM Standards, 1961*, Part 4. A list of the corresponding AASHO and ASTM test designations are:

Standard Tests	Designation	
	AASHO	ASTM
a. Mechanical Analysis of Soils	T 88	D 422
b. Liquid Limit of Soils	T 89	D 423
c. Plastic Limit of Soils	T 90	D 424
d. Calculating the Plasticity Index	T 91	D 424

C. Soil Classification

7.04 GENERAL

After the required laboratory tests have been performed for a given material, its proper soil group classification can be determined without much difficulty. Since an understanding of certain peculiarities and performance characteristics of the various soil groups is relevant to the correct use of the groups as highway materials, a more detailed discussion of the different soil groups is presented.

7.05 DIFFERENTIATION BETWEEN GRANULAR AND FINE-GRAINED SOILS

The mechanical analysis test is used to separate the granular soils from the fine-grained soils. The granular soils are classified as groups E-1 through E-5 and are distinguished from the fine-grained soils by the requirement that the granular soils must have less than 45 percent of combined silt and clay. All soils with 45 percent or more combined silt and clay are grouped as fine-grained soils and classified as soil groups E-6 through E-12. The fine-grained groups are listed in order of increasing liquid limits and plasticity indexes. The determination of the sand, silt, and clay soil fractions is made on the soil passing the No. 10 sieve, since this soil fraction usually represents the critical portion as far as moisture changes and other climatic influences are concerned. This determination further allows a textural classification to be made which has been useful in turf development and drainage facilities selection.

7.06 DESCRIPTION OF CLASSIFICATION GROUPS

a. Granular Soils:

Group E-1—Well-graded coarse granular soils that are stable even under poor drainage conditions and are not subject to detrimental frost heave. Soils in this group may conform to requirements for soil type base courses such as well-graded sand-clays with excellent binder.

Group E-2—Similar to E-1 but has less coarse sand and may contain greater percentages of silt and clay. Therefore, soils of this group may become unstable when poorly drained and may be subject to limited amounts of frost heave.

Groups E-3 and E-4—Include the fine sandy soils of inferior grading. They may consist of fine cohesionless sand or sand-clay types with a fair to good quality of binder. They are less stable than E-2 soils under adverse drainage and frost conditions.

Group E-5—Poorly graded granular soils having between 35 percent and 45 percent of combined silt and clay. This group also includes all soils with less than 45 percent of silt and clay but which have plasticity indexes greater than 10. A plasticity index greater than 15 would cause the soil to be classified with the fine-grained soils, even though it may contain more than 55 percent of sand.

b. Fine-Grained Soils:

Group E-6—Silts and silty loam soils having zero to low plasticity. These soils are friable and quite stable when dry or at low moisture contents. They lose stability and become very spongy when wet and for this reason are difficult to compact unless the moisture content is carefully controlled. Capillary rise in the soils of this group is very rapid; and they, more than soils in any of the other groups, are subject to detrimental frost heave.

Group E-7—Clay loams, silty clays, clays, and some sandy clays. They range from friable to hard consistency when dry and are plastic when wet. These soils are stiff and dense when compacted at the proper moisture content. Variations in moisture are apt to produce detrimental volume change. Capillary forces acting in the soil are strong, but the rate of capillary rise is relatively slow, and frost heave, while detrimental, is not as severe as in the E-6 soils.

Group E-8—Similar to E-7 soils, but the higher liquid limits indicate a greater degree of compressibility, expansion and shrinkage, and lower stability under adverse moisture conditions.

Group E-9—Silts and clays containing micaceous and diatomaceous materials. They are highly elastic and very difficult to compact. They have low stability in both the wet and dry state and are subject to frost heave.

Group E-10—Silty clay and clay soils that form hard clods when dry and are very plastic when wet. They are very compressible, possess the properties of expansion, shrinkage, and elasticity to a high degree, and are subject to frost heave. Soils of this group are more difficult to compact than those of the E-7 and E-8 groups and require careful control of moisture to produce a dense, stable fill.

Group E-11—Soils similar to E-10 but having higher liquid limits. This group includes all soils with liquid limits between 70 and 80 and plasticity indexes greater than 30.

Group E-12—Soils having liquid limits greater than 80 regardless of plasticity indexes. They may be highly plastic clays that are extremely unstable in the presence of moisture; or they may be very elastic soils containing mica, diatoms, or organic matter in excessive amounts. Whatever the cause of their instability, they will require the maximum in corrective measures.

Group E-13—Organic swamp soils such as muck and peat which are recognized by examination in the field. Their range in test value is too great to be of any value in a system of identification and classification. They are characterized by very low stability, very low density in their natural state and very high moisture contents.

7.07 MODIFICATIONS TO CLASSIFICATION OF SOIL

There are two modifications to be used when classifying soils by the correct soil group. These modifications (explained below) are to be used when the following conditions exist:

a. Test results on fine-grained soils, E-6 through E-12 inclusive, may place the soil, according to Table VII-1, in more than one group. This could happen with soils containing mica, diatoms, or a large proportion of colloidal material. When this overlapping of soil groups occurs, the test results are referred to Figure VII-1, and by the use of this figure in conjunction with Table VII-1, the appropriate soil group can be determined.

Soils with plasticity indexes higher than the maximum corresponding to the maximum liquid limit of the particular group are not of common occurrence. When encountered, however, they are placed in the higher numbered group as shown in Figure VII-1.

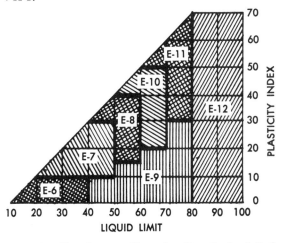

Figure VII-1—Classification Chart for Fine-Grained Soils.

b. The presence of material retained on the No. 10 sieve should serve to improve the over-all stability of the soil, since only that portion of the soil sample passing the No. 10 sieve is considered in the soil classification above. For this reason, upgrading the soil from one to two classes is permitted when the percentage of the total sample retained on the No. 10 sieve exceeds 45 percent for soils of the E-1 through E-5 groups and 55 percent for the remaining groups, provided the coarse fraction consists of reasonably sound material which is fairly well-graded from the maximum size down to the No. 10 sieve size. Stones or rock fragments scattered through a soil should not be considered of sufficient benefit to warrant upgrading.

7.08 FAA CLASSIFICATION PROCEDURE

The final classification of a soil in a particular soil group is accomplished by using the results obtained from the required tests of Section B and Appendix A in conjunction with Table VII-1. If modifications are required, the final classification is made by using Table VII-1, Figure VII-1, and by determining the amount of material retained on the No. 10 sieve as previously discussed. With the required test data available, enter Table VII-1, and determine the correct soil group by process of elimination. If the soil falls into more than one group as discussed in Article 7.07, then enter Figure VII-1, and determine the correct soil group; or if the portion of the sample passing the No. 10 sieve is considerable, adjust the classification as discussed in Article 7.07.

D. Subgrade Classification

7.09 GENERAL

In addition to the thirteen soil groups which have been described, the FAA has set up corresponding subgrade classes based on the performance of a particular soil as a subgrade for pavements under different drainage and frost conditions. The subgrade classes and their relationship to the soil groups are shown in Table VII-2. The prefix indicates subgrade classes for asphalt pavement structures.

Subgrades classed as Fa furnish adequate subgrade support without the addition of subbase material. Soils in group E-1 fall into the Fa subgrade class under all conditions of drainage and frost, while E-2 soils are classed as Fa subgrades only where the drainage is good. The other subgrade classes are designated F1 through F10. The soil's value as a subgrade material decreases as the number increases.

7.10 DISTINGUISHING DRAINAGE CONDITIONS

A knowledge of the topography of the construction site, the properties and arrangement of the different

Table VII-2—Airport Paving Subgrade Classification

Soil Group	Subgrade class			
	Good drainage		Poor drainage	
	No frost	Severe frost	No frost	Severe frost
E-1	Fa	Fa	Fa	Fa
E-2	Fa	Fa	F1	F2
E-3	F1	F1	F2	F2
E-4	F1	F1	F2	F3
E-5	F1	F2	F3	F4
E-6	F2	F3	F4	F5
E-7	F3	F4	F5	F6
E-8	F4	F5	F6	F7
E-9	F5	F6	F7	F8
E-10	F5	F6	F7	F8
E-11	F6	F7	F8	F9
E-12	F7	F8	F9	F10
E-13	Not suitable for subgrade			

layers of the soil profile, and the elevation of the ground water table are all required for a distinction to be made between good and poor drainage conditions.

Good drainage may be defined as a condition where: (1) the topography allows the surface water to be removed rapidly, (2) the internal drainage characteristics allow no accumulations of water that would cause spongy areas to develop in the subgrade, and (3) the ground water table is at such an elevation that the soil will not become waterlogged either by percolation or capillarity. All of the soil groups with the exception of E-13 can meet these conditions.

Poor drainage is defined as a condition for which the subgrade may be rendered unstable because of:

(1) topographic features, such as flat terrain at elevations only slightly above sea level, (2) the character of the soil profile, (3) capillary rise from a high ground water table, or (4) any other cause resulting in poor stability or saturation of the subgrade.

Good drainage cannot be distinguished from poor drainage on the basis of results of soil tests alone. Reliance upon soil tests alone has led to the erroneous conception that a good drainage condition cannot exist when the soils consist of clays and silty clays of the E-7 through E-12 groups. There is no logical reason for such an assumption, even though it is recognized that soils of these groups are expansive and subject to detrimental volume change with variations in moisture content. The degree to which these detrimental properties may develop will depend on the drainage conditions, as indicated by a study of the topography and the entire soil profile, and on capillary moisture.

It is important to remember that while the soil group may be determined by means of laboratory test results, the drainage conditions must be established by the subsurface and surface characteristics of the site.

7.11 NO FROST VS. SEVERE FROST

A severe frost condition is assumed to exist if the depth of frost penetration for the particular site is greater than the anticipated thickness of surface, base, and subbase for a "no frost" condition.

Some explanation may be necessary relative to a combination such as "good drainage" and "severe frost." Obviously, a good drainage condition may exist in a location where the average depth of frost penetration exceeds the required thickness of surface, base, and subbase for a "no frost" condition. In this case, the subgrade class would be determined on the basis of "severe frost." The importance of a "severe frost" condition in a location having good drainage has been questioned. From the standpoint of detrimental frost heave, that condition may not be important.

It is well known, however, that even under the best drainage conditions, the penetration of frost below the non-heaving subbase material, together with alternate freezing and thawing, produces a softening of the subgrade soil immediately under the subbase. The only remedy is additional subbase thickness to overcome the loss in stability.

The average annual frost penetration throughout the United States is shown in Figure VII-2 and intended as a guide only. The actual depth of frost penetration should be determined for each site on the basis of reliable local information.

7.12 FAA SUBGRADE CLASSIFICATION PROCEDURE

The final subgrade classification is obtained from the predetermined soil group, and the drainage and frost conditions existing at the particular site. With this information enter Table VII-2 and select the proper subgrade class.

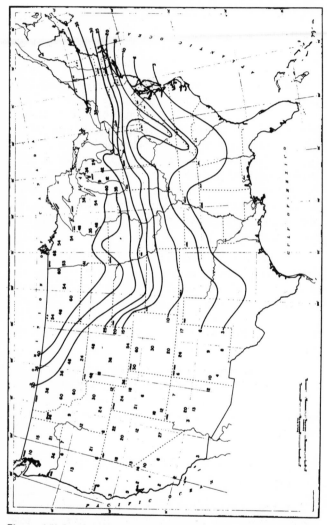

Figure VII-2—Average Depth of Annual Frost Penetration—
in Inches.

—Courtesy, Federal Aviation Administration

PART II

*Determination of Strength Values for Design
of Asphalt Pavement Structures*

Chapter VIII

CALIFORNIA BEARING RATIO (CBR) METHOD

A. General

8.01 DEVELOPMENT AND DEFINITION

The *California Bearing Ratio* (or CBR Method) with its numerous variations is probably the most widely used method of designing asphalt pavement structures. This method was developed by the California Division of Highways around 1930 and has since been adopted and modified by numerous states, the U. S. Corps of Engineers, and many countries of the world. The Corps of Engineers adopted this method during the 1940's, and their test procedure is most generally used, with and without certain modifications. In 1961, the American Society for Testing and Materials adopted the method as ASTM Designation D 1883, *Bearing Ratio of Laboratory-Compacted Soils*. The ASTM procedure differs in only minor respects from the Corps procedure. The Corps method has been followed rather closely in preparing this Chapter.

The CBR is a comparative measure of the shearing resistance of a soil. It is used with empirical curves to design asphalt pavement structures. This test consists of measuring the load required to cause a plunger of standard size to penetrate a soil specimen at a specified rate. The CBR is the load, in pounds per square inch, required to force a piston into the soil a certain depth, expressed as a percentage of the load, in pounds per square inch, required to force the piston the same depth into a standard sample of crushed stone. Usually depths of 0.1 inch or 0.2 inch are used, but depths of 0.3, 0.4, and 0.5 inch may be used if desired. Penetration loads for the crushed stone have been standardized. The resulting bearing value is known as the California Bearing Ratio, which is generally abbreviated to CBR, with the percent omitted.

8.02 SCOPE

This test method is intended to provide the relative bearing value, or CBR, of base, subbase, and subgrade materials. Procedures are given for laboratory-compacted specimens of swelling, nonswelling, and granular materials. Moreover, procedures are described for performing in-place field tests and tests upon undisturbed samples obtained from the field.

Tests on laboratory-compacted specimens are performed usually to obtain information which will be used for design purposes. The in-place field test can be used under certain conditions to determine the load-carrying capacity of material in place in the field. When the in-place field test is performed on materials which may later and during the life of the pavement undergo changes of moisture content, undisturbed samples of the field-compacted materials are tested in the laboratory for conditions of moisture content simulating those expected in the field.

8.03 AUXILIARY SOIL TESTS

There are certain routine soil tests which should be performed prior to conducting the CBR test. These tests are as follows:

Standard Tests	Designation	
	AASHO	ASTM
a. Sieve Analysis of Fine and Coarse Aggregate	T 27	C 136
b. Liquid Limit of Soils	T 89*	D 423*
c. Plastic Limit of Soils	T 90*	D 424*
d. Calculating the Plasticity Index	T 91*	D 424*
e. Mechanical Analysis of Soils (only for classification purposes)	T 88	D 422
f. Specific gravity of +4 material	T 85	C 127
g. Field density test	T 147	D 1556

1. The sample shall not be oven-dried, nor subjected to any artificial drying before processing for testing.

2. The sample shall be soaked in water for 24 hours prior to washing.

3. The sample shall be washed through the No. 40 sieve. Material retained on the sieve shall be dried, then dry-sieved through the No. 40 sieve. The portion dry-sieved through the No. 40 sieve shall be combined with the material washed through the sieve. This combination shall be used for the liquid limit and plastic limit tests.

4. The sample shall be set aside and the water decanted or wicked off. No chemicals shall be added to hasten settlement of the fines. The sample shall be dried to approximately the liquid limit with care being taken to prevent caking or lumping during the drying process. The liquid limit test shall be performed from wet of the liquid limit to dry of the liquid limit, using the mechanical method. No dry soil shall ever be added to the sample during performance of either the liquid limit or the plastic test.

5. Water content shall be further reduced by air drying and the plastic limit performed. Drying shall not proceed below the plastic limit. Care shall be taken to prevent caking or lumping during drying.

6. The plastic limit test shall be performed on a ground glass plate.

7. Modifications to the soaking time and to the method of hastening settlement of the fines will be made when check tests of the specification material show that the modifications do not affect results.

The AASHO procedures for all the above tests are described in detail in Appendix A, and the ASTM standard procedures may be found in the *ASTM Standards, 1961*, Part 4.

B. Determination of CBR for Remolded Specimens

8.04 GENERAL

The CBR value for a soil will depend upon its density, molding moisture content, and moisture content after soaking. Since the product of laboratory compaction should closely represent the results of field compaction, the first two of these variables must be carefully controlled during the preparation of laboratory samples for testing. Unless it can be ascertained that the soil being tested will *not* accumulate moisture and be affected by it in the field after construction, the CBR tests should be performed on soaked samples.

8.05 EQUIPMENT

The equipment and materials required for determining the CBR value of a soil consists of the items shown in Figures VIII-1 through VIII-3 and are described as follows:

a. *Cylindrical Mold*—6 in. inside diameter, 7 in. deep provided with a collar extension about 2 in. length. A perforated base plate with perforations not greater than 1/16 in. diameter is required for specimen preparation. A base plate without perforations is employed for compaction control tests.

The base plate and collar should be made to clamp on either end of the mold. For any group of molds, one extra base plate is desirable, since two plates are required when a mold is inverted during specimen preparation.

b. *Spacer Disc*—metal, 5 15/16 in. diameter x 2½ in. high.

c. *Compaction Hammer*—sliding weight or sleeve

type, 2 in. diameter steel tamping foot, 10 lb. weight with an 18 in. fall.

d. *Sieves*—¾ inch and a No. 4.

e. *Expansion Apparatus*—adjustable stem and perforated plate, tripod, and dial micrometer (reading to 0.001 inch) suitable for measuring the expansion of the soil.

f. *Weights*—one annular and several split 5 lb. weights, 5⅞ in. outside diameter and 2⅛ in. inside diameter, suitable to apply as surcharge loads on soil surface during soaking and penetration.

g. *Penetration Piston*—1.95 inch diameter face (three square inches) and sufficiently long to pass through the surcharge weights and penetrate the soil.

h. *Loading Device*—laboratory testing machine or screw jacks and frame arrangement which can be used to force the penetration piston (plunger) into the soil specimen at a uniform rate of 0.05 inch per minute.

i. Coarse filter paper, wire screen, and cellophane.

j. Equipment for conducting routine soil tests listed under Article 8.03.

k. *Miscellaneous Apparatus*—mixing bowls, dial micrometers, spatulas, straightedges, trowels, knives, spoons, scales, soaking tank, ovens, moisture content cans or boxes and stop watch.

8.06 SOIL PREPARATION

a. Air-dry the total sample until it becomes friable under a trowel. Approximately 75 lbs. of material passing the ¾-inch screen will be required.

b. Break up soil aggregations, being careful to avoid reducing the natural size of the individual particles.

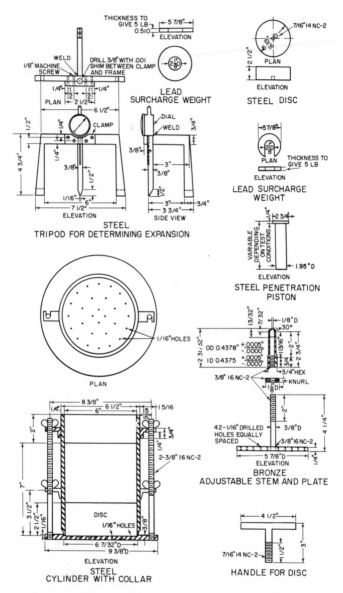

Fig. VIII-1—California Bearing Ratio Test Apparatus.

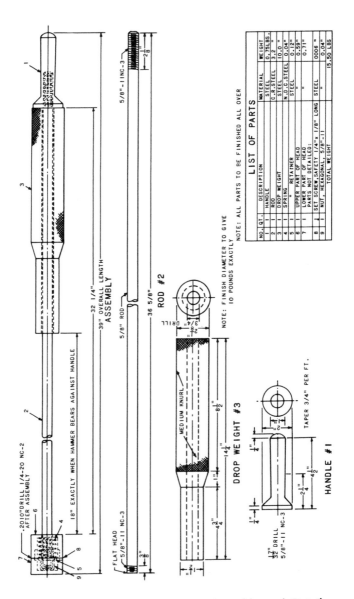

LIST OF PARTS

NO.	QT.	DESCRIPTION	MATERIAL	WEIGHT
1	1	HANDLE	STEEL	0.75 LBS.
2	1	ROD	C.R. STEEL	3.2 "
3	1	DROP WEIGHT	STEEL	10.0 "
4	1	SPRING RETAINER	N.D.C. STEEL	0.04"
5	1	" "	STEEL	0.12"
6	1	UPPER PART OF HEAD	"	0.59 "
7	1	LOWER PART OF HEAD PARTS NOT DETAILED:	"	0.71"
8	1	SET SCREW, SAFETY, 5/8"x 1/8" LONG	STEEL	0006 "
9	1	NUT, HEXAGONAL, 5/8"-11	"	0.04"
		TOTAL WEIGHT		15.50 LBS

NOTE: ALL PARTS TO BE FINISHED ALL OVER

ASSEMBLY

39" OVERALL LENGTH

32 1/4"

18" EXACTLY WHEN HAMMER BEARS AGAINST HANDLE

.2010"DRILL 1/4-20 NC-2
AFTER ASSEMBLY

ROD #2

5/8" ROD
36 5/8"
5/8"-1 INC-3

2 3/8"

FLAT HEAD
5/8"-11 NC-3

3/80"

3/8" DRILL

NOTE: FINISH DIAMETER TO GIVE
10 POUNDS EXACTLY

DROP WEIGHT #3

MEDIUM KNURL

14 1/4"

8 1/2"

1"

4 3/4"

2"

HANDLE #1

TAPER 3/4" PER FT.

4 1/2"

2 1/4"

1 1/4"

1 1/4"
3/8" DRILL
5/8"-11 NC-3

Fig. VIII-2(a)—Compaction Tamper: Assembly and Details.

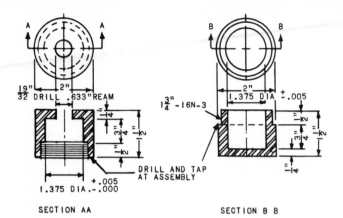

SECTION AA

SECTION B B

UPPER PART OF HEAD #6   LOWER PART OF HEAD #7

WIRE DIAMETER 10 GA.(0.135")
5 1/2"TOTAL NUMBER OF COILS
ENDS SQUARED AND GROUND.

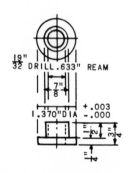

SPRING RETAINER #5

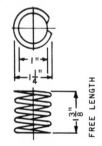

HAND DRAWN CARBON STEEL WIRE
SPRING #4

Fig. VIII-2(b)—Compaction Tamper: Assembly and Details

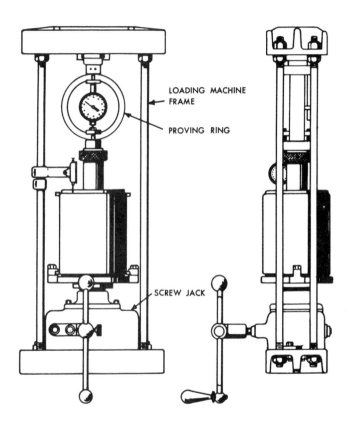

LOADING MACHINE FRAME

PROVING RING

SCREW JACK

Fig. VIII-3—Laboratory Loading Device.

Note: A convenient means of controlling the rate of penetration is to mount on the loading device a small electric motor geared to move the jack at exactly 0.05 inch per minute.

c. Separate the sample into three fractions over the ¾-inch and No. 4 sieves.

d. Discard all material retained on the ¾-inch sieve, and replace it with an equal portion of original material passing the ¾-inch sieve and retained on the No. 4 sieve.

e. Recombine and thoroughly mix the sample.

f. Place prepared soil sample in a moisture proof container.

g. Oven-dry approximately 500 grams of the material just prepared, to determine its moisture content. Moisture content is determined as follows:

$$w = \frac{W_1 - W_2}{W_2} \times 100$$

where w = moisture content in percent based on oven-dry soil weight.

W_1 = weight of wet soil.

W_2 = weight of oven-dry soil.

8.07 PROCEDURE FOR CONDUCTING THE COMPACTION CONTROL TEST

The compaction control test used by the Corps of Engineers is a modification of the Standard AASHO Designation T 99 and essentially corresponds to Method D, Designation T 180. Both of these test procedures are included in Appendix A. Modifications made by the Corps of Engineers are as follows:

a. The mold shall be as specified in Article 8.05 a.

b. The compaction hammer shall be of the sliding weight type. It shall consist of a two-inch diameter steel tamping foot, a ⅝-inch steel rod, a weight with an 11/16-inch hole through the center, and a handle. Construction of the tamping foot and weight shall be such that tamping blows can be applied adjacent to the sides of the mold. The rod shall be attached to the tamping foot with a spring cushion. The maximum allowable weight of the assembled compaction hammer is 17½ pounds.

c. The preparation of the soil shall be as described in Article 8.06.

d. No material shall be re-used, and a separate batch shall be used for each compaction test specimen.

e. The desired amount of mixing water for each test specimen shall be added, mixed well, and the material placed in a container with an airtight cover and allowed to cure for 24 hours. The water content should be redetermined if appreciable condensation occurs on the container wall.

f. Clamp the mold and detachable collar extension to the base plate, insert the spacer disc, and place a coarse filter paper on top of the disc.

g. Compact the specimen in five one-inch layers, each layer receiving the required number of blows of the specified tamper or hammer.

h. For cohesive materials, the water content tested shall range from below to above the estimated optimum; for cohesionless materials, the water content shall range from air-dried to as high as practicable.

i. Modifications to the above procedures may be made when check tests on the specified materials show that the modifications do not affect the results.

j. Place the mold assembly on a concrete floor or pedestal during compaction.

k. Compact a sufficient number of test specimens over a range of water contents to definitely establish the optimum water content and the maximum density. If compaction characteristics of the material are fairly well known, four or five specimens compacted at water contents within the range of $\pm 2\%$ of optimum water content are usually enough to establish the optimum water content and the maximum density.

1. Plot the test results in the form of a moisture-density diagram, and draw a smooth curve through the points. Figure VIII-4 shows typical moisture-density diagrams for compaction tests made with 55 blows per layer (modified AASHO T 180 Method D) and for 26 and 12 blows per layer. A suggested form for use in recording test data is shown in Figure VIII-5.

8.08 PREPARATION OF TEST SPECIMENS

a. Assemble the 6-inch mold, extension collar, and perforated base plate by clamping the mold with fitted extension collar to the base plate.

b. Insert the spacer disc over the base plate, and place a 6-inch diameter coarse filter paper on top of the disc.

c. Compact samples using compacting efforts and molding water content as indicated below. Specimens are usually compacted at several moisture contents and densities to cover the anticipated range that will be experienced in the field. In preparing remolded specimens for the CBR method of design, all subgrades and base courses have been grouped into three classes with respect to behavior during saturation: (a) cohesionless sands and gravels, (b) cohesive soils, and (c) highly swelling soils. The first group usually includes the GW, GP, SW, and SP classifications.* Swelling soils usually comprise the MH, CH, and OH classifications. Separate procedures for sample preparation are given for each of the groups.

---

* Unified Soil Classification System.

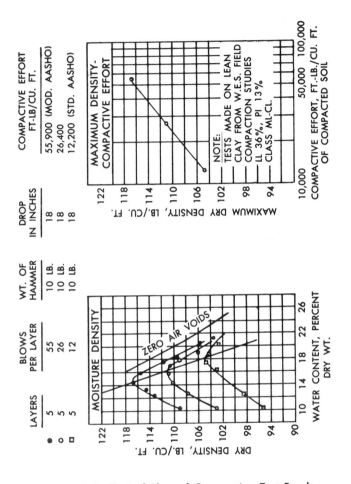

Figure VIII-4—Typical Plots of Compaction Test Results.

1. *Cohesionless sands and gravels.* Cohesionless soils usually compact readily under rollers or traffic, and specimens should be prepared at high densities and at a range of water content

covering those anticipated in the field and including water contents as high as practicable. Using predetermined and plotted moisture-density relationship, compact samples (using the same procedures as outlined for compaction control test in Article 8.07) at optimum moisture content, and on the wet and dry side of

COMPACTION CONTROL TEST					
PROJECT ARDMORE AFB				DATE 9 JUNE 52	
SAMPLE NO. 3243				JOB NO. 32181	
INITIAL WATER CONTENT, v_o = __4.5__ %		AS MOLDED		SOAKED ✓	
__55__ BLOWS PER EACH OF __5__ LAYERS __10__ -LB HAMMER __18__ -IN. DROP					

Specimen		A	B	C	Remarks
Desired dry weight	W_s'	5000			
1 + v_o		1.045	1.	1.	Subgrade Material
Soil weight W_s' $(1+w_o)=$	W_o	5225			
Bowl tare	W_b				
$W_o + W_b$					
Test water content	w'	6 %	%	%	
Add water, W_s' $(v' - v_o)$		75			
Mold		4			
Weight mold + Soil	W	14787			
Mold tare	W_m	10742			
Less tare, $W - W_m$ =	W_c	4045			
Average water content	w	53 %	%	%	
Mold Constant	C	0.0298	0.	0.	
Wet density, CW_c =	m	120.5			
Dry density, $m \div 1 + w =$	i	114.4			

WATER CONTENTS	A		B		C	
Tare	4	29				
Tare + wet soil	159.8	180.3				
Tare + dry soil	153.0	172.5				
Water W_w	6.8	7.8				
Tare	25.3	25.4				
Dry soil W_s	127.7	147.1				
Water Content w	5.3 %	5.3 %	%	%	%	%

Densities in pounds per cubic foot. Weights in grams.

TECHNICIAN ACB 011157 B	COMPUTED SSW	CHECKED TH

Figure VIII-5—Suggested Form for Recording Compaction Test Data

optimum. Molding moisture content may be obtained by drying a portion of the sample (100 grams for clays and 500 grams for gravelly soils) at the time the specimen is compacted. Soaking may be omitted in subsequent tests on the same material if it does not lower the CBR. Usually the lowest CBR value obtained from this series of specimens is used as the design CBR.

2. *Cohesive Soils.* Soils in this group are compacted and tested in a manner to develop data that will show their behavior over the entire range of anticipated moisture contents for representative samples. Compaction procedures are similar to those outlined in Article 8.07, except that compaction curves are developed for 55, 26, and 12 blows per layer and each specimen is soaked and penetrated to develop a complete family of curves showing the relationship between density, water content, and CBR. To aid in determining the validity of the compaction data, a semilog plot of maximum density versus compaction effort in work per unit volume usually gives a straight-line relationship. The data from a CBR test are plotted as shown in Figure VIII-6, and the resulting family of CBR curves represents the characteristics encompassing a wide range of field conditions. The design CBR should be based on the density and molding-moisture content anticipated in the field. For example, assume that the lean clay soil, for which results are plotted in Figure VIII-6, can be processed to an average moisture content from 13 to 16 percent and that it can be compacted to a density varying from 110.5 (95 percent of AASHO T 180 Method D maximum density) to 115 pounds per cubic foot (see cross-hatched area on left plot). If construction could be controlled so that the density and moisture

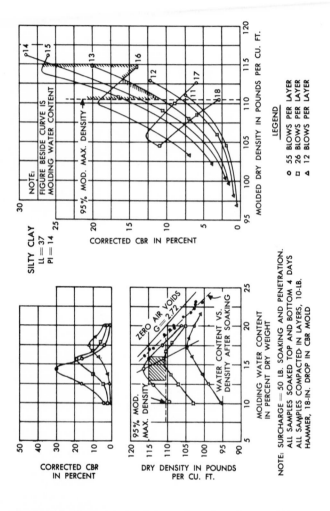

Fig. VIII-6—Recommended Procedure for Plotting CBR Test Data for Design.

— 114 —

were within these ranges, the right-hand plot would indicate that the soils, after moisture conditions had become adjusted, would have a CBR (see crosshatched area on right plot) varying between about 11 (110.5 pounds per cubic foot and 13 percent moisture) and 26 (115 pounds per cubic foot and 15 percent moisture). The design CBR would be selected near the lower figure, say 12 percent. The right-hand plot shows that close control of moisture content within these limits (13 to 16 percent) is necessary because low CBR values will be obtained if the moisture content during rolling is allowed to increase appreciably above the desired range. For example, if the moisture content is allowed to increase one percent, to 17 percent, the right-hand plot indicates the CBR (at 95 percent AASHO T 180 Method D maximum density) would decrease from 26 to 8. Another percent increase in moisture would result in a CBR of about 3.

3. *Swelling Soils.* The sample preparation procedures for highly swelling soils are the same as previously described for cohesive soils; however, the objectives of the testing program are not exactly the same as for cohesive soils. Tests are performed on soils with expansive characteristics to determine a moisture content and a unit weight which will minimize expansion. The proper moisture content and unit weight are not necessarily the optimum moisture content and unit weight determined by AASHO T 180 Method D compaction tests. Generally, the minimum swell and highest soaked CBR will occur at a molding moisture content slightly wetter than optimum. It may be necessary, when testing highly swelling soils, to prepare samples for a wide range of moisture contents in order to establish the relationship between

moisture content, density, swell, and CBR for a given soil.

Moisture, density, and CBR data should be plotted as shown on Figure VIII-6 just as for cohesive soils. In addition, percent of swell should be plotted versus molding water content for the various compaction efforts in the same way that CBR and density are shown in the plots on the left of Figure VIII-6. A comparison of the plots of swell, CBR, and density versus molding water content will permit selection of specification limits for moisture and density. This also will permit the limitation of swell and, at the same time, give the greatest values of CBR and density which might reasonably be obtained. Then, just as for cohesive soils, design CBR and density values would be selected toward the bottom of the ranges in CBR and density, consistent with the specification limits selected.

Where it is desirable to limit swell by the addition of overburden load, tests will have to be conducted to determine the amount of load necessary. These tests can consist of additional specimens, prepared for soaked CBR tests, using various added amounts of surcharge during soaking. The amount of surcharge required to limit swell to a permissible amount then can be used to compute the needed thickness of overburden. The same result may be accomplished with fewer specimens by restricting the swell during soaking and measuring the pressure developed.

d. After each sample has been compacted in the mold, remove the extension ring; strike off excess soil with a straightedge; remove the base plate; and extract the spacer disc.

e. Weigh the mold and compacted soil to determine the density of soil.

f. Place filter paper on the base plate; invert the cylinder so that the bottom during compaction is now on top; re-attach to the base plate; and place filter paper on top of soil in mold.

g. Place the perforated aluminum plate, with adjustable stem attached, on the filter paper.

h. Place surcharge weights on the aluminum plate to produce an intensity of surcharge loading equal to the weight of the base material and pavement within ± 5 pounds, but not less than 10 pounds.

i. Immerse the mold and weights in water to within ½ inch of the top of the mold. Place blocks under the mold to allow free access of water to the bottom of the specimen, and put water inside the mold to the same level as water on the outside of the mold.

j. After immersion, measure the height of the stem or spindle above the edge of the mold with the dial micrometer and tripod assembly. This is the initial measurement for swell.

k. Allow the specimen to soak for four days, maintaining constant water level outside and inside the mold.

l. Repeat step j to obtain the final swell measurement. Compute the swell as a percentage of the initial specimen height.

Example

Swell Data

Reading after 4 days	.	.	.	.	.	0.405 in.
Original reading	.	.	.	.	.	0.388 in.
Swell (difference)	.	.	.	.	.	0.017 in.

$$\text{Swell (\%)} = \frac{\text{swell}}{\text{ht. of specimen}} \times 100 = \frac{100 \times 0.017}{5} = 0.34\%$$

m. Remove the mold from the water, and pour off free water from inside the mold, being careful not to disturb the soil.

n. Remove the surcharge weights, perforated plate, and filter paper, and allow the specimen to drain for 15 minutes.

o. Weigh the specimen to determine the soil density. The specimen is then ready for the penetration test.

8.09 PROCEDURE FOR PENETRATION TESTING

Note: This procedure is the same for all types of remolded specimens. Moreover, it is also applicable for undisturbed and field in-place tests after the testing surface has been prepared.

a. Place one 5-pound annular disc surcharge weight on the soil surface.

b. Place the mold in the loading frame or hydraulic press, and adjust its position until the piston is centered on the specimen.

c. Seat the penetration piston with a 10-pound load, and set both the load dial and strain dials to zero. This initial load is required to insure satisfactory seating of the piston and should be considered as the zero load when determining stress-penetration relations.

d. Add penetration surcharge weights to produce an intensity of loading equal to the weight of the base material and pavement (within ± 5 pounds), but not less than 10 pounds. If the sample has been previously soaked, the surcharge should be equal to the soaking surcharge.

e. Apply the load to the piston at a uniform rate of 0.05 inch of penetration per minute.

f. Record the total load readings at 0.025, 0.050, 0.075, 0.100, 0.125, 0.150, 0.175, 0.200, 0.250, and 0.300 inches penetration. A suggested form for recording test information is shown in Figure VIII-7.

CALIFORNIA BEARING RATIO TEST									
Penetration									
PROJECT ARDMORE AFB						DATE 13 JUNE 52			
SAMPLE NO. 3243						JOB NO. 3218.1			
NO. BLOWS 55					AS MOLDED	SOAKED ✓			
MOLD NO. 4			Soaking 30		Surcharge weights, in pounds: Penetration 30				
Date	Time	Days	Reading Inches	Swell Inches	Swell %	BEARING RATIO DATA (3 sq-in. piston. 0.05 in. per min.)			
						Penetration Inches	Load Lb	Bearing Value* Lb-In.-2	Bearing Ratio %
9 June	2 PM	0	0.763	0.					
10 June	2 PM	1	0.901	0.					
13 June	2 PM	4	0.916	0.153	3.40	0.025	5	1.67	Corr
			0.	0.		0.050	40	13.34	CBR
			0.	0.		0.075	70	23.34	%
			0.	0.		0.100	95	31.67	37.5
			0.	0.		0.125	115	38.34	
WATER CONTENTS AFTER SOAKING	Whole Specimen Drained		Top Inch			0.150	140	46.67	
						0.175	160	53.34	
Tare No.	7		20			0.200	180	60.00	42.4
Tare + wet soil	505 7		199.5			0.250	210	70.00	
Tare + dry soil	444 2		173.8			0.300	250	83.34	
Water	615		25.7			0.350			
Tare	652		25.5			0.400			
Solids	3790		148.3			0.450			
Water Content	16.2 %		17.3 %			0.500			
* 0.734 X Load in Kilograms, Load in Pounds ÷ 3									
Remarks Subgrade material. Test should be rerun because CBR at 0.2-in. penetration is larger than CBR at 0.1-in. penetration.									
TECHNICIAN 011157 A S.S.W.		CHECKED A.C.B.				DATE T.H.			

Figure VIII-7—Suggested Form for Recording CBR Test Information

g. Release the load; remove the mold from the loading device; remove the weights; and detach the base plate.

h. For laboratory tests, determine the average moisture content for the entire depth of the sample. For field tests, take a sample of soil from the top inch for moisture content.

i. Remove and discard the remaining soil.

j. From the loads obtained in f, the CBR of the sample is determined, as illustrated in Section E.

C. Tests on Undisturbed Specimens

8.10 GENERAL

Tests on undisturbed samples may be used for design where the natural condition is the controlling factor. They may also be used for correlation of field in-place test results with design moisture. For the latter condition, duplicate samples should be obtained. One should be tested at natural or in-place water content and the other at design water content to determine the correction to be applied to the results of the in-place tests, i.e., the reduction in CBR that occurs during the soaking should be applied as a correction to the results of the field in-place tests.

8.11 EQUIPMENT

The equipment required for determining the CBR of undisturbed specimens consists of the items listed below:

a. Equipment required for CBR penetration test in the laboratory as previously described.

b. Compaction Molds, CBR: as previously described. To be used for obtaining samples of soft fine-grained soils that will completely fill the mold.

c. *Sampling Collar:* Edge sharpened for cutting through soil.*

d. *Metal Split Jacket Mold:* 7-inch diameter and 7 inches high.*

e. *Wooden Box:* Removable top and bottom.

f. *Wax Paper or Paraffin.*

g. *Miscellaneous Apparatus:* Shovel, saw, knives, resin, adhesive tape, heating apparatus, and can for heating paraffin.

8.12 OBTAINING A SAMPLE WITH CBR MOLD

a. Smooth the ground surface, and press the sampling collar, mold, and extension collar into soil with moderate pressure, holding disturbance of the specimen to a minimum.

b. Excavate a trench around the mold, and press the mold down firmly over the soil.

c. Trim soil away from the sampling collar with a knife by cutting downward and outward to avoid cutting into the sample.

d. Excavate the trench deeper and repeat the above procedure until the soil is well into the extension collar. (If stones interfere, pick out carefully and backfill with soil, making note of this in sample log.)

e. Cut off the sample at the bottom of the mold with a knife, shovel, or saw and remove from the hole.

f. Remove the extension collar, and trim the top surface of the soil level with the ends of the mold. Remove the sampling collar, and repeat trimming process. Trimmings, or samples from an adjacent hole, can be used for moisture content determinations.

---

* These are usually improvised by the laboratory.

g. Protect both ends with paraffin or wooden discs, and tape around the edges and over sides of mold. Wrap in a damp cloth to prevent moisture loss while transporting to the laboratory.

h. The dry unit weight of the sample may be obtained by means of a field density test performed in an adjacent hole.

8.13 OBTAINING SAMPLE WITH SPLIT JACKET

A split jacket cylinder should be used (Figure VIII-8) for soils that cannot be sampled with the CBR mold.

a. Smooth the ground surface. On the surface, mark the outline of the soil chunk to be sampled, excavate a trench around chunk, deepen the excavation, and trim sides of the chunk with a butcher knife. Obtain moisture content samples from the trimmings.

b. Trim the sample to a size slightly smaller than the jacket, and place jacket over sample.

Figure VIII-8—Method of Sampling with Steel Cylinders.

Courtesy Corps of Engineers

c. Fill the sides and top of the sample with warm paraffin and 10 percent resin.

d. Cut off the bottom of the sample, remove the jacket and sample from the hole, trim sample surfaces, and seal the ends with paraffin and resin for transportation to the laboratory.

e. The dry unit weight of the sample may be obtained by means of a field density test performed in an adjacent hole.

8.14 OBTAINING A BOX SAMPLE

This method of sampling is recommended for gravelly soils. An undisturbed sample is obtained with an open-ended wooden box in a manner similar to that used for obtaining a split jacket sample. The sample is encased on all sides, top and bottom, in a thick layer of paraffin, and then a wooden top and bottom are placed on the box for shipment to the laboratory. Moisture content and dry unit weight may be obtained in an adjacent hole.

8.15 PREPARATION OF SAMPLES FOR CBR TESTING

a. In the case of compaction mold samples, remove the protective cover from one end of the sample, and trim or fill with sand to produce a surface that is flush with the end of the mold. Then place a wire screen or filter paper over the trimmed end of the sample, and attach the perforated base plate. Invert the mold, remove the protective covering from the other end, and smooth this surface also. Attach the extension collar, and the sample is ready for soaking.

b. For samples in the split jacket, loosen bolts, expand the jacket, and loosen the sample from sides. Extrude the sample so that it extends about one inch beyond the end of the jacket, and then reclamp.

Remove exposed paraffin with a knife, and carefully trim the sample down to the rim of the jacket. Again, loosen the bolts, and lower the sample back to the original position. Tighten the bolts, and the sample is now ready for soaking.

c. For box samples, remove the top, and carefully cut away paraffin. Level the surface with sand.

d. The procedure for soaking undisturbed specimens is the same as for laboratory-compacted specimens.

8.16 PROCEDURE FOR PENETRATION TESTING

The specimens shall be penetrated as described in Article 8.09 and the CBR value calculated as shown in Section E, Calculations.

D. Field In-Place Tests

8.17 GENERAL

The field in-place test is, under certain conditions, a satisfactory test for determining the load-carrying capacity of a material in place in the field. Basically, the penetration phase of this test is the same as described previously. The field in-place test may be used under any one of the following conditions:

a. When the in-place density and water content are such that the degree of saturation (percentage of voids filled with water) is 80 percent or greater.

b. When the material is coarse-grained and cohesionless so that it is not affected by changes in water content.

c. When the material has been in place for several years. In cases such as this, the water content does not actually become constant but appears to fluctuate within rather narrow ranges, and the field in-place test is considered a satisfactory indicator of the load-carrying capacity. The time required for the water content to stabilize cannot be stated definitely, but the minimum time is about three years.

Three in-place CBR tests should be performed at each elevation tested in the base course and at the surface of the subgrade. However, if the results of these three tests do not show reasonable agreement, three additional tests should be made. A reasonable agreement between three tests, where the CBR is less than 10, permits a tolerance of 3; from 10 to 30, a tolerance of 5; and from 30 to 60, a tolerance of 10. Above a CBR of 60, variations in the individual readings are not of particular importance. For example, actual test results of 6, 8, and 9 are reasonable and can be averaged as 8; results of 23, 18, and 20 are reasonable for an average of 20. If the first three tests do not fall within this tolerance, then the three additional tests are made at the same location, but not the same spot, and the numerical average of the six tests is used as the CBR at that location. Generally, CBR values below about 20 are rounded off to the nearest point; those above 20 are rounded off to the nearest 5 points.

8.18 EQUIPMENT

The apparatus for field testing, as shown in Figures VIII-9 and VIII-10, consists of the following:

a. *Loading Device:* Mechanical screw jack to apply load, truck jacks, and loaded truck to provide resistance for screw jack.

b. *Penetration Piston:* 1.95-inch diameter (three-square-inch face area), six-inch length, with internally threaded pipe extensions and connectors.

c. *Dial Micrometers and Support.*

d. *Surcharge Weights:* Described in Article 8.05 f.

e. *Calibrated Proving Rings.*

f. *Steel Plate:* 10-inch diameter, 10 pounds in weight with a 2 1/32-inch diameter hole in the center.

g. Small channel beam or other rigid beam at least six feet long for use as a datum plane for measuring penetration.

h. *Miscellaneous Equipment:* Stop watch, pick, shovel, knives, spoons, moisture content cans, and straightedge.

8.19 TEST PROCEDURE

a. Select a test site with no exposed stones larger than ¾ inch, level the surface, and remove all loose material.

b. Position the truck over the test site, and jack up so there will be no load on the rear axle.

c. Place the required surcharge weights in the center of the test area, and set the assembled test apparatus in position as shown in Figure VIII-10.

d. Then follow the procedure described in Article 8.09 a-g.

e. After completion of the test, obtain soil samples at the point of penetration for in-place moisture content determmniation.

f. Make an in-place density determination at a point about 4 to 6 inches away from the point of penetration.

E. Calculations

8.20 STRESS-STRAIN CURVE

After the test has been completed, the penetration unit load in psi is calculated and the stress-strain curve plotted on cross-section paper. In order to obtain true

Figure VIII-9—Field in-place California Bearing Ratio apparatus (unassembled).

Figure VIII-10—Typical Field CBR Set-up. *Courtesy Virginia Council of Highway Investigation and Research*

penetration loads from the test data, the zero point of the curve is adjusted to correct for surface irregularities and the initial concave upward shape of the curve if it is present. If the curve is uniform as in example No. 1 of Figure VIII-11, the CBR value is calculated from the recorded loads. For surface irregularities as in example No. 3 of Figure VIII-11 extend the straight line portion of the curve to the base to obtain a corrected origin, or zero. If the curve has a reverse bend, or concave upward shape, as in example No. 2, draw a line tangent to the steepest point of the curve (point A), and extend the line to the base to obtain a corrected origin or zero point (point B). Then read the corrected load values for 0.1-inch penetration (point C) and 0.2-inch penetration (point D).

8.21 CALCULATION OF CALIFORNIA BEARING RATIO

The CBR value is defined as a ratio comparing the bearing of a material with the bearing of a well-graded crushed stone. The penetration loads for crushed stone are presented in the following table:

Penetration in Inches	Standard Load (Lbs.)	Standard* Load (PSI)
0.1	3000	1000
0.2	4500	1500
0.3	5700	1900
0.4	6900	2300
0.5	7800	2600

* Plunger cross-section area = 3 square inches.

The corrected load values, obtained as prescribed in Article 8.20, are determined at 0.1-inch and 0.2-inch pene-

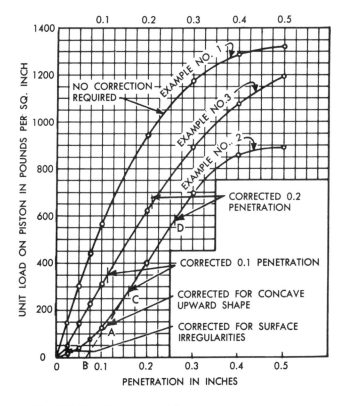

Fig. VIII-11—Correction of Stress-Penetration Curves.

tration from which the CBR values are determined by use of the following formula:

$$CBR\ (\%) = 100\ \frac{x}{y} \qquad\qquad x = \frac{aD}{3}$$

where,   x = soil resistance or the unit load on

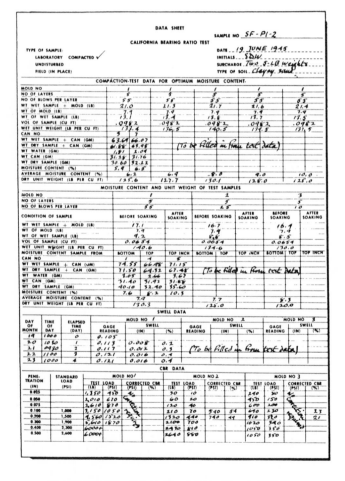

Figure VIII-12—Example of Data Sheet, CBR Test

the piston, psi. (for 0.1 inch of penetration interval)

y = standard unit load, psi.

a = value of one dial division, lbs.

D = actual dial reading

The CBR is determined from the corrected load values at 0.1- and 0.2-inch penetrations by dividing the loads at 0.1 and 0.2 inch by the standard loads of 1000 and 1500 pounds per square inch, respectively. Each ratio is multiplied by 100 to obtain the CBR in percent. The CBR is usually selected at 0.1-inch penetration. If the CBR at 0.2-inch penetration is greater, the test should be rerun. If check tests give similar results, the CBR at 0.2-inch penetration should be used.

Chapter IX

BEARING VALUE DETERMINATION (PLATE BEARING TEST)

A. General

9.01 DESCRIPTION

Plate bearing tests are used by a number of organizations for the design and evaluation of asphalt pavement structures. The test procedures employed may vary somewhat between agencies. Since Asphalt Institute manuals refer to the ASTM plate bearing test procedure, the method described here is ASTM Designation: D 1195, "Repetitive Load Tests of Soils for Use in Evaluation and Design of Airport and Highway Pavements."

The plate bearing test can be used to measure the strength at any elevation in an asphalt pavement structure: surface of the subgrade, top of the subbase, top of the base course, or surface of the finished pavement.

Like all other soil strength tests, a plate bearing test will not provide a representative measurement of subgrade strength unless it is made when the soil is in the same condition as that expected after equilibrium with the environmental influences of moisture, density, frost, drainage, and traffic. Equilibrium is not attained until some time after the pavement has been superimposed over it. When the strength of the subgrade soil for a new highway or airport pavement is required, this may be achieved by one or the other of the following methods:

a. Perform the plate bearing test on the subgrade beneath an existing asphalt pavement where the same subgrade soil occurs, and where the pavement has been in place long enough for the subgrade to have reached equilibrium with its environment.

b. Perform the plate bearing test on a specially constructed test section of the soil, where an adequate depth has been processed to duplicate the conditions expected after it reaches equilibrium with its environment following the paving operation.

When The Asphalt Institute manuals refer to the plate bearing test as the basis for thickness design requirements for highways and airport runways, the criteria are as follows:

a. For highways—

1. 12-inch diameter bearing plate

2. 0.2-inch deflection

3. 10 repetitions of load

b. For airport runways—

1. 30-inch diameter bearing plate

2. 0.5-inch deflection

3. 10 repetitions of load

9.02 DEFINITIONS

The terms deflection, residual deflection, and rebound deflection, as used in this chapter, are defined as follows:

a. *Deflection*—the amount of downward vertical movement of a surface due to the application of a load to the surface.

b. *Residual Deflection*—difference between original and final elevations of a surface resulting from the application and removal of one or more loads to and from the surface.

c. *Rebound Deflection*—the amount of vertical rebound of a surface that occurs when a load is removed from the surface.

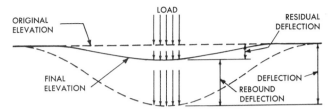

LOAD

ORIGINAL
ELEVATION

RESIDUAL
DEFLECTION

FINAL
ELEVATION

DEFLECTION

REBOUND
DEFLECTION

Figure IX-1—Diagram Illustrating the Difference Between
Deflection, Residual Deflection and Rebound Deflection

B. Plate Bearing Test

9.03 GENERAL

Before the plate bearing test is started, the following
things should be done:

a. Obtain topographical data throughout the proposed area to be paved.

b. Classify the subgrade soil using one of the appropriate soil classification systems.

c. Perform the following field and laboratory tests:

1. The in-place density test described in Appendix A.

2. Moisture content, mechanical analysis, Atterberg limits, and the AASHO compaction test for
moisture-density relations.

The procedures for all of the above tests are found in
Appendix A.

9.04 EQUIPMENT

Equipment for the plate bearing test includes a loading device, a hydraulic jack assembly, bearing plates, and
the necessary dial gauges, mounts, and miscellaneous
tools.

The loading device can be a truck, trailer, a combination of both a tractor and trailer, an anchored frame, or other structure. It is loaded with sufficient weight to produce the desired reaction on the surface under test. The supporting points (wheels in the case of a truck or trailer) should be at least eight feet from the circumference of the largest diameter plate being used.

The hydraulic jack assembly includes a spherical bearing attachment capable of applying and releasing the load in increments. The jack shall have sufficient capacity for applying the maximum load required, and shall be equipped with an accurately calibrated gauge that will indicate the magnitude of the applied load.

The bearing plates shall be steel circular plates not less than one inch in thickness and having diameters ranging from six inches to 30 inches. The plates shall be machined so that they can be arranged in pyramid fashion to insure rigidity.

Note: A minimum of four different plate sizes is recommended for pavement design or evaluation purposes. For evaluation purposes alone, a single plate may be used, provided that its area is equal to the tire contact area for the most critical combination of conditions of wheel load and tire pressure. For providing data indicative of bearing index (for example, the determination of relative subgrade support throughout a period of a year), a single plate of any size may be used.

The equipment shall include two or more dial gauges, graduated in units of 0.001 inch, capable of recording a maximum deflection of one inch.

The equipment includes a beam upon which the dial gauges are mounted. The beam should be a 2½-inch standard black pipe or a 3 by 3 by ¼-inch steel angle, or equivalent. It should be as least 18 feet long and should rest on supports located at least 8 feet from the circumference of the bearing plate or the nearest wheel or supporting leg.

Miscellaneous tools include a spirit level for use in preparing the surface to be tested and for levelling the bearing plates, dial gauge clamps or holders; a stop watch, fine sand, and plaster of Paris.

9.05 PLATE BEARING TEST PROCEDURE

a. Carefully center a bearing plate, of the selected diameter, under the jack assembly. This plate is set level in a thin bed of a mixture of fine sand (60%) and plaster of Paris (40%), of plaster of Paris alone, or of fine sand, using the least amount of material required for uniform bearing of the plate. Refer to Figures IX-2 and IX-3.

b. Place the remaining plates of smaller diameter concentric with, and on top of, the bearing plate.

c. Where unconfined load tests are to be made at a depth below the surface, remove all of the surrounding material to provide a clearance equal to one and one-half plate diameters from the edge of the bearing plate, Figure IX-2. For confined tests, the diameter of the excavated circular area must be just sufficient to accommodate the selected bearing plate, Figure IX-3.

d. The average vertical movement of the bearing plate is obtained from dials whose stems rest on the upper surface of the bearing plate. If two dials are used, place them one inch from the ends of a diameter of the plate. If three dials are used, place them 120 degrees apart and one inch from the periphery of the bearing plate.

e. After the equipment has been properly arranged, seat the bearing plate assembly. This is accomplished by the quick application and release of a load sufficient to produce a deflection of not less than 0.01 inch or more than 0.02 inch as indicated by the dial gauges. When the dial needles come to rest following release of this

— 137 —

Figure IX-2—Loading on the Subgrade with a 12-inch Plate After Removing Pavement (Unconfined Test)—*Courtesy, Kentucky Dept. of Highways*

Figure IX-3—Loading on the Subgrade with a 30-inch Plate After Removing Pavement (Confined Test)

load, reseat the plate by applying one-half the recorded load producing the 0.01- to 0.02-inch deflection. When the needles have again come to rest, set each dial accurately at its zero mark. A typical arrangement of equipment for a plate bearing test is illustrated in Figure IX-4.

> Note: The use of additional dial gauges placed on the surface of the material being tested at ½, 1, and 1½ bearing plate diameters from the edge of the bearing plate, is optional.

f. Apply a load giving a deflection of about 0.04 inch, start a stop watch, and maintain the same load constantly until the rate of deflection is 0.001 inch per minute or less for three successive minutes. Then completely release the load, and observe the rebound until the rate of recovery is 0.001 inch per minute or less, for three successive minutes. Apply and release the same load in this manner ten times. Record the readings of the dial gauges, resting on the bearing plate, at the end of each minute. Record the readings of the dial gauges set beyond the perimeter of the bearing plate just before the application, and just before the release of load, for each repetition. To ensure good contact between the gauges and the bearing plate, or other surface on which they are resting, buzz an electric bell attached to the deflection beam for 10 seconds before the dials are to be read.

g. Increase the load to give a deflection of about 0.2 inch, and proceed as directed in the immediately preceding paragraph.

h. Increase the load to give a deflection of about 0.4 inch, and proceed as before.

i. In all cases the standard end point shall be a rate of deflection or of recovery of 0.001 inch per minute or less for three successive minutes.

j. The deflection for a given load at any time is determined by averaging the readings of the dial assembly on the bearing block.

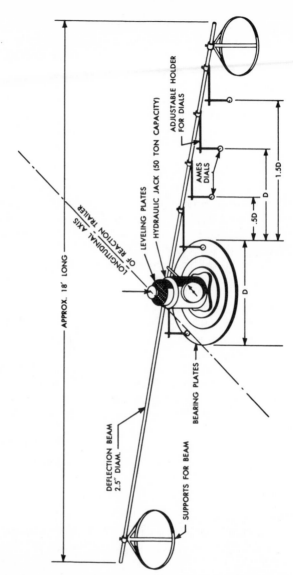

Figure IX-4—Diagram Showing Arrangement of Equipment for Plate Bearing Test.

Location—Midcontinent Airport
    ₵ of Runway 7-25
      Station 6+40

Personnel—E. M. Kennedy
           C. S. Brown
           E. L. Smith

Weather—Clear and warm

Load Test on—Subgrade

Time—11:00 a.m. ....p.m.

Dia. Bearing Plate—30 in.

Test Begun—11 hr. 04 min.

Jack No.—1,125,642

Test Finished—16 hr. 38 min.

Gauge No.—023-352,416

Seating Load—3000 lbs.

Seating Deflection—0.018 in.

Reseating Load—1500 lbs.
(Deflection Gauges Zeroed)

Corrected Reseating Load—1394 lbs.
Dead Load—Plates, Jack, etc.—474 lbs.

Time
11:00 11:30 12:00 12:30 13:00 13:30 14:00 14:30 15:00 15:30 16:00 16:30

Temp. °F
 72   75   80   84   88   91   92   89   87   86   83   81

Applied Load Gauge Reading lbs.	Number of Load Application or Release	Time		Deflection Readings			
				Gauge 1	Gauge 2	Gauge	Average
		hr.	min.	in.	in.	in.	in.
34,000	First Application	11	04	0.3090	0.2260	—	0.2675
			05	0.3254	0.2410	—	0.2832
			06	0.3344	0.2480	—	0.2912
			07	0.3390	0.2522	—	0.2956
			08	0.3450	0.2564	—	0.3007
			09	0.3488	0.2596	—	0.3042
			10	0.3510	0.2614	—	0.3062
			11	0.3550	0.2646	—	0.3098
			12	0.3570	0.2660	—	0.3115
			13	0.3596	0.2680	—	0.3138
end point deflection—0.3184 in.			14	0.3614	0.2700	—	0.3157
			15	0.3630	0.2718	—	0.3174
			16	0.3640	0.2728	—	0.3184
			17	0.3650	0.2738	—	0.3194
			18	0.3658	0.2746	—	0.3202
0	First Release		19	0.2830	0.2070	—	0.2450
			20	0.2330	0.1592	—	0.1961
			21	0.2312	0.1576	—	0.1944
			22	0.2300	0.1558	—	0.1929
			23	0.2290	0.1550	—	0.1920
end point rebound deflection—			24	0.2282	0.1540	—	0.1911
0.1920 in.			25	0.2280	0.1536	—	0.1908

Figure IX-5—Field Load Test Data Sheet.

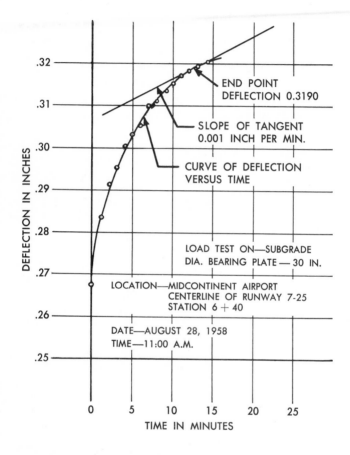

Figure IX-6—Graphical Method for Obtaining Deflection
Value where Rate of Deflection is 0.001 inch per minute.

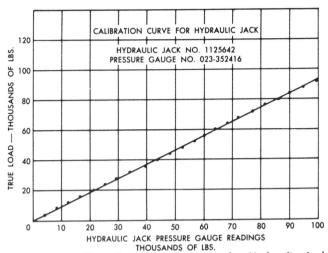

Figure IX-7—Typical Calibration Curve for Hydraulic Jack

Location—Midcontinent   Airport
    ₵ of Runway 7-25
        Station 6 + 40
Date—August 28, 1958
Time—11:00 a.m.
Corrected Reseating Load—1394 lbs.

Load Test on—Subgrade
Dia. Bearing Plate—30 in.

Jack No.—1,125,642
Gauge No.—023-352,416
Wt. of dead load, plates, jack,
    etc.—474 lbs.

Applied Load				Measured Deflection Values in Inches For Load Application No.					
Jack Reading				1	2	3	4	5	6
Gauge lbs.	Corrected lbs.	Dead Load lbs.	Corrected Total Load						
10,000	9,300	474	9,774	.0439	.0513	.0534	.0562	.0577	.0590
24,000	22,300	474	22,774	.1583	.1775	.1897	.1974	.2041	.2099
34,000	31,600	474	32,074	.3184	.3685	.4078	.4371	.4562	.4741

Figure IX-8—Data Sheet Listing Measured Deflection Values
for Each of Six Applications of Each Load.

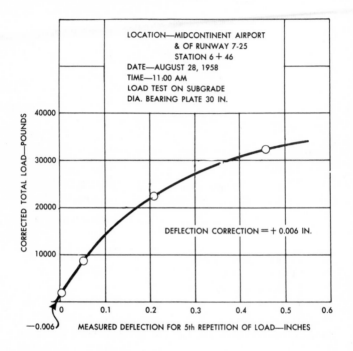

Figure IX - 9 —Determination of the Zero Point Correction for Deflection Measurement.

k. From a thermometer suspended in the shade near the bearing plate, read and record the air temperature at half-hour intervals.

l. In addition to the recording of load, deflection, and temperature data, a record should be made of the following:

1. Date and weather conditions.

2. Test personnel and duties.

3. Time at start and end of the test.

4. Any irregularity in routine procedure.

5. Any unusual conditions observed at the test site, and any unusual happenings during the actual test.

See Figure IX-5 for an example of a data sheet for recording load test data during a plate bearing test.

9.06 CALCULATION AND PLOTTING OF LOAD —DEFLECTION RELATIONSHIPS

a. For each repetition of each load, determine the deflection at which the rate of deflection is exactly 0.001 inch per minute. This is termed "end point deflection" and can be determined from visual inspection of the deflection data for each repetition of load recorded, Figure IX-5. If desired, the deflection at which the rate of deflection is exactly 0.001 inch per minute can be obtained graphically by plotting deflection versus time readings for each application of each load, as illustrated in Figure IX-6. The point on the deflection versus time curve at which the tangent to the curve represents rate of deflection of 0.001 inch per minute is the end point deflection. Note, however, that the end point deflection obtained by the laborious graphical method of Figure IX-6 (for the time deflection data of Figure IX-5) is the same for practical purposes as that read off from Figure IX-5 by visual inspection of the field data.

Location—Midcontinent Airport   Load Test on—Subgrade
          ₵ of Runway 7-25   Dia. Bearing Plate—30 in.
              Station 6 + 40
Date—August 28, 1958   Jack No.—1,125,642
Time—11:00 a.m.   Gauge No.—023-352,416
              Deflection Correction—+0.006 in.

Corrected Total Load lbs.	Corrected Deflection Values in Inches For Load Application No.					
	1	2	3	4	5	6
9,774	.0499	.0573	.0594	.0622	.0637	.0650
22,774	.1643	.1835	.1957	.2034	.2101	.2159
32,074	.3244	.3745	.4138	.4431	.4622	.4801

Figure IX-10—Data Sheet Listing Corrected Deflection Values
for Each of Six Applications of Load.

b. The applied loads, read from the pressure gauge of
the hydraulic jack, must be corrected by means of a
calibration curve for the jack and pressure gauge (illustrated in Figure IX-7). The applied loads also must be
adjusted for the dead load of the bearing plates, jack, etc.
When this is done, tabulate corrected total load versus
measured deflection at which the rate of deflection is
exactly 0.001 inch per minute, for each repetition of each
load, Figure IX-8.

c. Using the data from Figure IX-8, determine the
zero point correction for the measured deflections by
plotting the corrected total loads versus measured deflections for the fifth repetition of load, Figure IX-9.
The corrected total load for zero measured deflection
is the corrected reseating load plus the dead load of the
bearing plates, jack, etc., (1868 pounds).

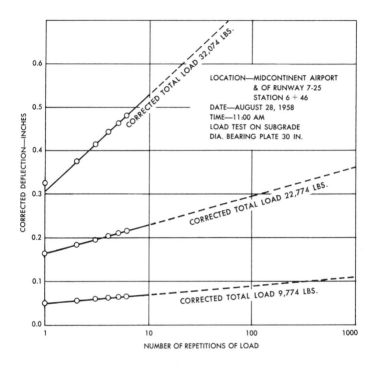

Figure IX – 11—Influence on Deflection of Repetitions of Loading for Each of Three Magnitudes of Load.

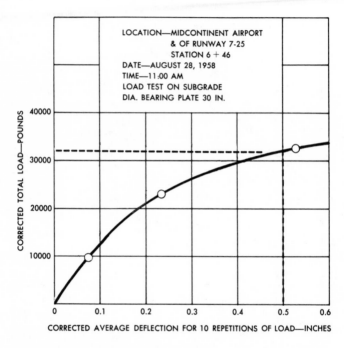

Figure IX - 12—Corrected Total Load Versus Corrected Deflection for 10 Repetitions of Load.

d. Add the zero point correction for deflection (0.006 inch) to each of the measured deflections listed in Figure IX-8. Then tabulate for each repetition of each load corrected total load versus corrected deflection at which the rate of deflection is exactly 0.001 inch per minute, Figure IX-10.

e. Plot the corrected deflection data versus number of repetitions of each corrected total load listed in Figure IX-10 on a semi-logarithmic graph, Figure IX-11. Straight lines are drawn through the plotted points and are projected beyond ten repetitions of load. The point for one repetition of load often must be ignored when drawing the best straight line. Similar graphs may be prepared in which either corrected residual deflection or corrected rebound deflection are plotted versus the number of repetitions of each corrected total load.

f. After selecting the required data from Figure IX-11, plot corrected total load versus corrected deflection for 10 repetitions of load as illustrated by Figure IX-12. From Figure IX-12, the bearing value at 0.5 inch deflection for 10 repetitions of load is easily determined as shown (32,000 lbs.).

g. If a bearing value based upon a greater number of repetitions is desired either more repetitions of each load may be applied to the plate, or the curves of Figure IX-11 may be extrapolated as shown, to obtain deflection values for the desired number of repetitions.

Chapter X

HVEEM'S RESISTANCE VALUE (R) METHOD

A. General

10.01 DEVELOPMENT AND APPLICATION

This method of evaluating treated and untreated materials for bases, subbases and subgrades for pavement thickness design was developed by F. N. Hveem and R. M. Carmany of the California Division of Highways. This method is currently used by the highway departments of at least four Western states in addition to the California Division of Highways. The R-value method of design is based on two separate measurements:

a. The *R-value* (or resistance value) determines the thickness of cover or structural section required to prevent plastic deformation of the soil under imposed wheel loads.

b. The expansion pressure test determines the thickness or weight of cover required to maintain the compaction of the soil.

The design R-value is determined from the moisture content and density at which these two thicknesses are equal. With granular non-expansive soils, the design R-value is determined for a density considered to be equivalent to that which will be obtained by normal construction compaction. This density value is obtained from the exudation pressure data.

The method of test for determining the R-value consists of the following parts:

a. Preparation of the samples.

b. Compaction of the test specimen.

c. Determination of exudation pressure of test specimens.

d. Determination of the expansion pressures of the test specimens.

e. Determination of the R-value.

Each of these parts will be presented separately and in the proper order for correctly performing the complete test. Since each of these determinations is made on the same specimen, and are required to properly determine the design R-value, they must be made in the order listed. The procedures described in this chapter are essentially the same as those found in *Laboratory Manual for California Test Procedures* (*Test Method 301*), published by the Materials and Research Department, California Division of Highways, Sacramento, California. Similar procedures may be found in AASHO Standard Methods of Test: Designations T 173, T 174, and T 175.

B. Preparation of Soil Samples

10.02 GENERAL

This preliminary part of the evaluation describes the preparation methods (batching, mixing, and curing) of soil samples which have been obtained by approved soil sampling techniques.

10.03 EQUIPMENT

The equipment required for the preparation of the soil samples is as follows:

a. *Sample Splitter:* Chutes ¾ inch wide.

b. *Scales:* 5,000 grams and 500 grams capacity accurate to 1.0 gram and 0.1 gram respectively.

c. *Miscellaneous Equipment:* Metered water spray can, mixing pans, trowels, ½-gallon cans with tight fitting lids, and a set of standard sieves.

d. *Test Record Forms:* Assign one specific form to an individual specimen, and keep it with the specimen until the R-value is obtained.

10.04 PREPARATION OF SAMPLE

a. Break down all clay lumps so that they pass the No. 4 sieve, and remove coatings from coarse aggregates.

b. Since the stabilometer test is made on relatively small samples, remove all large-size material according to the following criteria:

1. If 75 percent or more of the sample passes a ¾-inch sieve, remove the material retained on the ¾-inch sieve.

2. If less than 75 percent passes a ¾-inch sieve, remove all material retained on the one-inch sieve.

c. Separate that portion of the sample which passes the No. 4 sieve into approximate quantities needed for each of four specimens by means of a sample splitter.

d. Weigh out exact amounts of the material passing No. 4 sieve, and combine with the coarse portions to produce the desired gradation in four 1200-gram samples.

The following are examples of computations for combining the materials:

Example 1

Example with single sample. Given an aggregate in which the following grading is desired:

— 153 —

Sieve	As used percent passing
¾ in.	100
⅜ in.	89
No. 4	78

Calculate the percentage of ¾ inch to ⅜ inch, ⅜ inch to No. 4 and passing No. 4 material and multiply each percentage by the total weight of test specimen desired:

Sieves	Percent of each size		Weights for 1200 g. sample	
¾ in. to ⅜ in .	100 — 89 =	11	.11 × 1200 =	132
⅜ in. to No. 4 .	89 — 78 =	11	.11 × 1200 =	132
Passing No. 4		78	.78 × 1200 =	936
	Total	100%	Total	1200 g.

Example 2

Example with two samples to be combined. Given two samples having the gradings and combination as shown:

Sieve	As received percent passing		Proportioned grading		Combined percent passing	As used (remove + ¾ in.) percent passing
	Sample		80 percent No. 1	20 percent No. 2		
	No. 1	No. 2				
1 in.	100	100	80	20	100	
¾ in.	90	100	72	20	92	100
⅜ in.	80	95	64	19	83	90
No. 4	70	90	56	18	74	80

Check the sum of the components against the "As used" column. They may disagree by 1 percent because fractions have been rounded off:

Sieves	Sample No. 1	Sample No. 2	Check
¾ in. . . .	$\dfrac{100}{92} \times 72 = 78$	$\dfrac{100}{92} \times 20 = 22$	$78 + 22 = 100$
⅜ in. . . .	$\dfrac{100}{92} \times 64 = 70$	$\dfrac{100}{92} \times 19 = 21$	$70 + 21 = 91$
No. 4 . . .	$\dfrac{100}{92} \times 56 = 61$	$\dfrac{100}{92} \times 18 = 20$	$61 + 20 = 81$

Calculate the percentage of ¾ inch to ⅜ inch, ⅜ inch to No. 4 and passing No. 4 material and multiply each percentage by the weight of test specimen desired:

Sieves	Sample No. 1	Sample No. 2
¾ in. to ⅜ in. -	$(78\text{-}70) \times \dfrac{1200}{100} = 96$ g.	$(22\text{-}21) \times \dfrac{1200}{100} = 12$ g.
⅜ in. to No. 4 -	$(70\text{-}61) \times \dfrac{1200}{100} = 108$ g.	$(21\text{-}20) \times \dfrac{1200}{100} = 12$ g.
Passing No. 4 -	$(61\text{-}0) \times \dfrac{1200}{100} = 732$ g.	$(20\text{-}0) \times \dfrac{1200}{100} = 240$ g.
	936 g. $+$	264 g $= 1200$ g

e. Adequately identify each sample as it is proportioned, and add to each of the four samples ½ to ⅔ the amount of water necessary to saturate the sample as described later under Article 10.04 g.

1. Perform this operation by mixing the material with a hand trowel in a circular pan and, at the same time, rotating the pan horizontally beneath a fine water spray. Continue mixing for one minute after the water has been added.

2. Record amount of water added. Place each sample of loose material in a covered container, and allow to stand overnight.

f. For all materials to be tested, weigh out an extra sample of 200 grams or more, having exactly the same grading as the test samples, for the determination of initial moisture. Determine the moisture content by weighing accurately before and after drying to constant weight at 230°F.

g. Mixing:

1. The R-value test requires the preparation of four test briquettes at different moisture contents. The first briquette is used as a pilot specimen. After completing the pilot specimen, it can be used as a guide in the preparation of the other three stabilometer specimens which shall, when possible, conform to the following limitations:

Height = 2.5 inches ± 0.1 inch.

Exudation pressure: One sample should be above and two below 300 psi or two above and one below 300 psi.

2. All samples should exude moisture between 100 and 800 psi, except when very high expansion pressures are expected. In the latter case, wetter specimens are sometimes necessary to get expansion pressures low enough to provide an intersection with the R-value curve.

3. On the day following the overnight curing period, add additional moisture in the same

manner as described above in paragraph e, until the estimated saturation moisture is attained. Mix well while adding water, and continue mixing for one minute thereafter.

4. Weigh out enough material to fabricate a compacted specimen 4 inches in diameter and 2½ inches high.

5. Immediately cover the pan to prevent loss of moisture before compacting the test specimens.

h. Precautions:

1. Exercise care in splitting and batching the passing No. 4 mesh fractions to insure a minimum loss of dust from the sample. Tests have shown that differences in the amount of fines can have a profound effect on the R-value test.

2. Complete and thorough mixing of the sample during the process of adding water is essential for uniformity of test results. The period of mixing required in paragraph e above must be observed as the minimum requirement. However, to avoid excess moisture loss due to evaporation, do not continue mixing longer than two minutes after the adding of water has ceased.

3. At all times except during immediate processing, keep the samples in covered containers to prevent evaporation loss of moisture.

Notes: The determination of the proper soil weight-moisture relationships of test specimens, which is needed to meet the requirements of the R-value test, requires judgment and experience on the part of the operator. An estimation of the weight of material and moisture must be made for the pilot or trial briquette,

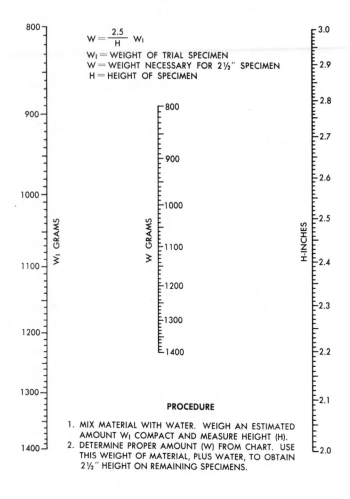

$$W = \frac{2.5}{H} W_1$$

$W_1 =$ WEIGHT OF TRIAL SPECIMEN
$W =$ WEIGHT NECESSARY FOR 2½" SPECIMEN
$H =$ HEIGHT OF SPECIMEN

PROCEDURE

1. MIX MATERIAL WITH WATER. WEIGH AN ESTIMATED AMOUNT W_1 COMPACT AND MEASURE HEIGHT (H).
2. DETERMINE PROPER AMOUNT (W) FROM CHART. USE THIS WEIGHT OF MATERIAL, PLUS WATER, TO OBTAIN 2½" HEIGHT ON REMAINING SPECIMENS.

Figure X-1—Chart for Determining Amount of Material for 2½" R-Value Briquette.

and its exudation pressure and height must conform to paragraph g above. Then, from the attached chart (Figure X-1), use the pilot specimen data, and determine the approximate weight of material for a 2½-inch high stabilometer specimen. From the exudation pressure of the pilot specimen, determine whether to use more or less moisture in the remaining samples to obtain the desired results. The decision as to the amount of water to use still rests with the operator. If the pilot specimen conforms to the requirements for a stabilometer specimen, it may be used as such; otherwise, it should be discarded.

Normally three specimens are enough to determine the R-value. However, in the case of critical materials, it is sometimes necessary to make additional tests in order that the true shape of the exudation pressure curve will be known at the "300 psi" exudation point. The exact number of tests needed is a matter of judgment.

C. Compaction of Test Specimen*

10.05 GENERAL

Specimens prepared by the compaction method described in the following paragraphs are designed to give test results indicative of the performance of the material when placed by construction equipment and subjected to traffic. The compaction procedure is a kneading action accomplished by use of the mechanical kneading compactor as developed by the California Division of Highways. This kneading action is intended to give the soil particles the orientation and contact pressure obtained during field compaction.

* See AASHO Test Designation: T 173.

Figure X-2—Mechanical Compactor.

10.06 EQUIPMENT

The apparatus required for the compaction of the test specimens is as follows:

a. *Mechanical Kneading Compactor** (see Figure X-2).

---

* Note: Working drawings may be obtained from the California Division of Highways, Materials and Research Department, 5900 Folsom Blvd., Sacramento, California; or the compactor is available from August Manufacturing Co., 1466 36th Avenue, Oakland 1, California.

b. *Compactor Accessories:* 4 inches inside diameter x 5 inches high steel molds, moldholder, mold funnel, feeder-trough 20 inches long, and a spatula (see Figure X-3).

c. *Heavy Paper and Cardboard Discs:* 4 inches in diameter.

d. *Rubber Disc:* 4 inches in diameter made from gasket material.

e. *Perforated Discs:* Phosphor bronze.

f. *Basket Fabrication Equipment:* A basket-making device consisting of a $3\frac{7}{8}$-inch diameter cylindrical wooden block, $\frac{1}{2}$-inch masking tape dispenser, $\frac{1}{2}$-inch-width masking tape, strips of notched paper, and phosphor bronze perforated discs that are used in the standard method of determining exudation pressure. Appendix A contains Method No. Calif. 904-B, Method of Fabricating Paper Baskets for Stabilometer Specimens.

10.07 COMPACTION PROCEDURE

a. Place mold in moldholder that has a rubber disc 4 inches in diameter and $\frac{1}{8}$ inch in thickness cemented to the plate. Adjust the mold for $\frac{1}{8}$-inch clearance between the lower edge of the mold and the base of the moldholder. Clamp in place. Place a 4-inch diameter cardboard disc into the mold on top of the rubber disc. Put the mold funnel in place, position the assembled moldholder on the compactor turntable, and lock it on studs.

b. Place well-mixed sample in the compactor feeder-trough with the loose material distributed evenly along the full length.

c. Start the compactor, and adjust the air pressure to 15 psi. Operate the compactor in accordance with instructions for operation and calibration of

Figure X-3—Compaction Procedure.

the mechanical compactor (Method No. Calif. 901).

d. Using a spatula formed to fit the feeder-trough, push the material in the lower three inches of the trough into the mold to cover the bottom. Push the remainder of the sample into the mold in 20 equal parts using one part for each blow of the compactor, see Figure X-3. Allow 10 additional blows to level and seat the material. Raise and clean compactor foot. Place rubber disc, 4 inches in diameter, ⅛-inch thick, on top of the specimen. (During the feeding operation, if the soil pushes up around the foot markedly, lower the air pressure below 15 psi to a pressure which will reduce the pushing.)

e. Lower the compactor foot, and immediately increase air pressure to the calibration gauge reading required to obtain a compactor foot pressure of 350 psi. On compactors that are so equipped, the green indicator light will flash on when the exact foot pressure of 350 psi is reached.

f. Apply 100 tamps to the specimen (using 350 psi foot pressure).

g. Clays and clean sands may require lower compaction pressures. In these cases, use the greatest compaction pressure possible, but do not allow the foot to penetrate over ¼ inch into the surface of the specimen after all the material is in the mold.

h. If free water should appear around the bottom of the mold during compaction, stop the compactor immediately and note the number of tamps.

i. If the surface is left uneven by the action of the tamping foot, smooth and level the tamped surface with a 1½-inch diameter flat-ended compaction rod using a gentle tamping.

j. Some granular materials are very difficult to handle without damage and may require a paper basket to keep the specimen intact. Baskets prevent the specimen from falling out of the mold and prevent crumbling when the specimen is transferred from the mold to the stabilometer. Compact all standard graded aggregate bases in baskets.

k. Baskets are designed to restrain the specimen as little as possible during the stabilometer test. For that reason, great care must be exercised in fabricating them with four strips of tape to hold them together.

l. When compacting a specimen in a basket, place all of the soil in the mold before lowering the foot. Use 100 tamps (350 psi pressure), and then remove the mold from the compactor. The mold should be kept upright so that the specimen will not fall out.

10.08 PRECAUTIONS

a. It is quite important that the operator feed the material into the mold from the trough in a uniform manner. Tests have shown that differences in compactive effort can cause variations in the results obtained from the exudation device when certain types of materials are tested. As an aid toward uniform feedings, it is suggested that the 20 increments be indicated on the edge of the trough with permanent scribe marks.

b. Even distribution of the coarse aggregates throughout the length of the feeder-trough is important in order to avoid segregation in the compacted specimen. The material should be evened out and leveled manually with the fingers or spatula along the trough before starting the feeding operations.

c. The decision whether to use baskets on a given material must be based on experience. They should not be used if they are not needed. If baskets are not used and the specimen breaks up while being transferred into the stabilometer, the fact may not be apparent at the time, but it will result both in excessive stabilometer pressure readings and in excessive displacement readings. Both of these errors tend to lower the R-value, and a group of three tests will be erratic with respect to one another. When this happens, the test must be repeated using baskets.

d. Caution must be exercised in the operation of the compactor so as not to allow any object other than the sample itself to intercede between the compactor foot and the mold at any time while the ram is in motion. The clearance between the inside edge of the mold and the compactor foot is approximately 1/16 inch. The applied shearing force of 1,100 pounds could cause severe injury to an operator's hand if caught between the compactor foot and the mold.

D. Determination of Exudation Pressure of Test Specimens

10.09 GENERAL

This part of the test procedure is used to determine the compressive stress necessary to exude water from the compacted specimen. Results from tests on the several specimens are used to determine the R-value at a standard pressure of 300 psi.

10.10 EQUIPMENT

The equipment required for determining the exudation pressure of the test specimens is as follows:

a. *Compression Testing Machine:* Capacity of at least 10,000 pounds.

b. Moisture exudation indicating device* (see Figure X-4).

c. *Follower Ram:* Metal, 4 inches in diameter (outside) x 6 inches high.

d. *Disc:* Phosphor bronze, perforated edge, 4 inches in diameter, 28 gauge.

e. *Filter Paper:* 4 inches in diameter.

10.11 PROCEDURE

a. Place the bronze disc on top of the tamped specimen in the mold, and then place one piece of filter paper on the disc.

b. Invert the mold with sample so that the filter paper is on the bottom, and place the mold on the contact plate of the moisture exudation indicator, making sure that it is centered firmly against both spring posts. In the case of a basket sample, do not

---

* Available from Harold F. Smith Tool and Die Shop, 2830 N Street, Sacramento 16, California.

invert the sample prior to placing on contact plate; simply put a filter paper on the bronze disc, and put the mold on the contact plate.

c. Place the contact plate with sample mold on the the platen of the testing machine centering the assembly to insure even loading. Turn on the moisture exudation indicator switch, and the center indicator light will then be lit, provided that the mold is both clean and in the correct position.

d. If the testing machine has a spherically seated type of upper head, use the proper shims to lock it in such a manner that the contact face is fixed firmly in a horizontal plane.

e. Place the follower ram on top of the sample, and force the sample down in the mold to the contact plate using either hand pressure or the testing machine.

f. Use the testing machine to apply an increasing load at the rate of 2,000 pounds per minute until five of the six outer lights are on. Convert the total load at that instant to psi and record as the exudation pressure. However, if free moisture becomes visible around the bottom of the mold and at least three outer lights are on, record the load in psi at that moment as the exudation pressure in lieu of waiting until five of the outer lights are on.

Figure X-4—Moisture Exudation Indicating Device.

g. Discard the specimen if the exudation pressure is found to be less than 100 or more than 800 psi, with the exception that very expansive material may require an exudation pressure of less than 100 psi.

h. Leave the test specimen in a covered mold for at least one-half hour after determination of the exudation pressure before beginning the next part of this test method.

10.12 PRECAUTIONS

a. The batteries in the moisture exudation indicating device must be replaced every three months to insure efficient operation.

b. When the exudation contact plate becomes worn or grooved and the contact points become raised or depressed, the plate should be replaced. These defects can affect the results without it becoming immediately apparent to the operator.

c. Care must be taken that moisture does not seep around the contact points, since this would cause electrical shorts to occur in the wiring and result in erroneous exudation pressures. Detection of this condition may be difficult, since the shorting is often not complete until the contact plate is loaded during the test. A check may be made by using a 4-inch diameter dry felt pad ½ inch or more thick in the place of the test specimen. If after loading, any lights go on, the plate should be replaced.

d. The operator must wipe the contact plate dry between tests, since any moisture remaining will prematurely dampen the new filter paper and cause erroneous exudation pressure results.

10.13 NOTES

a. Occasionally, material from exceptionally heavy clay test specimens will extrude from under the mold and around the follower ram during the loading operation. Yet, when the 800 psi point is reached, less than five lights are lit. When this occurs, the soil is of very poor quality and should be reported as having an R-value less than five.

b. There are many cases where high quality materials of a gravelly-sandy nature, such as untreated bases, will have exudation pressures that are extremely sensitive to slight changes in moisture content. Very often these pressures will appear erratic and out of step with the sequence of moistures. However, these materials generally exhibit uniform R-values having relatively small variation throughout the entire range of exudation pressures and moisture contents. The R-value exudation curve is drawn as an average value in these cases.

E. Determination of Expansion Pressure of Test Specimens*

10.14 GENERAL

This part of the complete test procedure is to be utilized in determining the expansion pressure a soil will develop in the presence of free water. This expansion pressure test is performed in such a way that a large change in specimen density does not occur during the test. Pavement thicknesses required to withstand these expansion pressures can be determined and compared with those determined by means of the R-value.

10.15 EQUIPMENT

a. *Expansion Pressure Device:*** With accessories as shown in Figures X-5 and X-6.

b. *Deflection Gauge:* With divisions of 0.0001 inch.

---

* See AASHO Designation: T 174.
** Available from Harold F. Smith Tool and Die Shop, 2830 N Street, Sacramento 16, California.

c. *Proving Ring:* With known capacity per 0.0001 inch deflection.

d. *Allen Wrench.*

e. *Filter Paper:* Fast type, 11-centimeter diameter.

10.16 EQUIPMENT CALIBRATION*

a. Properly adjust the brass shims under the spring steel bar of the expansion pressure device. This is done to maintain the correct relationship between the deflection of the spring steel bar and the expansive force generated by the test specimen. The proper adjustment is determined by means of the proving ring.

b. Calibrate the expansion pressure device at least bi-monthly as follows:

1. Place the dial indicator assembly in position on top of the expansion pressure frame. The single bearing end must rest on the adjustment plug.

2. Place a ¾-inch diameter ball bearing in the center hole of the expansion pressure device turntable.

3. Place the proving ring (indentation down on ¾-inch diameter ball) in the expansion pressure frame, centering the small ball on top of the proving ring under the expansion pressure dial contact.

4. Rotate the turntable up until the proving ring dial reads zero. Set the adjustment plug so that the expansion pressure dial reads zero.

---

* The method of calibrating the expansion pressure devices by using proving rings is no longer used by the California Division of Highways laboratories. The new procedure provides for direct calibration of expansion pressure devices by use of a counter type weighing scale modified to accommodate the expansion pressure device (Method No. Calif. 903-B dated January, 1960, see Appendix A). However, the old method of using a proving ring is still acceptable.

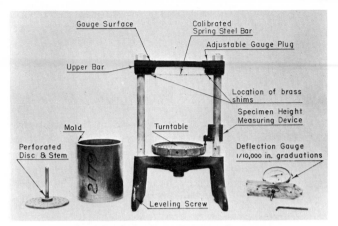

Figure X-5—Expansion Pressure Apparatus.

Figure X-6—Expansion Pressure Procedure.

5. Increase the pressure in steps of 0.0010 inch from 0 to 0.010 inch on the expansion pressure dial. The expansion pressure dial must check the proving ring dial within a tolerance of ± 0.0002 inch at every point.

6. If the dials do not check within the above tolerance, loosen the top frame bar, and adjust the position of the shims between the frame and the spring steel bar, until the desired check is obtained.

7. Remove the proving ring, and set the adjustment plug until the indicating dial reads 0.0010 inch from zero.

10.17 TESTING PROCEDURE

a. Allow the specimen to set for at least one-half hour after completion of the exudation test.

b. Determine the gross weight of the specimen for density calculations. Tare weight of the mold is determined prior to the performance of this test.

c. Place the deflection gauge in position on top bar of the expansion pressure device. Use an Allen wrench to raise or lower the adjustment plug until the deflection gauge is on minus 0.0010 inch. (The deflection gauge will now be on 0.0090.)

d. Place the stem and perforated brass plate firmly into position on the face of the compacted specimen in the mold.

e. Put the mold on the turntable in the expansion pressure device after first placing a filter paper on the turntable.

f. Turn up the turntable on the expansion pressure device until a surcharge deflection of 0.0010 inch is applied to the specimen. If the device was calibrated properly, the indicating dial should read zero.

g. Put approximately 200 ml. water on the specimen in the mold, and allow expansion pressure to develop for 16 to 20 hours.

h. At the end of the soaking period, read the deflection of the calibrated spring steel bar to 0.0001 inch. If any water has drained through specimen into the water trap (pan), pour the water back on top of the specimen, and allow it to begin percolating through the specimen before pouring off the excess water.

i. Remove the mold with the specimen, and pour off the excess water, and record whether the water drained freely through the specimen into the pan below.

j. Determine the expansion pressure using the following equation:

$$P = kd$$

where:
    $P =$ **expansion pressure shown by the soil, psi.**

    $k =$ **constant of spring steel bar calibrated from the proving ring (psi per 0.0001 inch).**

    $d =$ **deflection to 0.0001 inch shown by the indicating dial.**

10.18 PRECAUTIONS

a. Keep the gauge surfaces on the top bar and contact surfaces on the spring steel bar clean and polished. Since deflection measurements are taken to 0.0001 inch, dust and corrosion on any of the gauge contact points can result in erroneous measurements.

b. Keep the expansion pressure devices free from the influence of any source of vibration during the test. If shelving is used to hold the devices, do not attach or brace it to any of the building walls.

c. Before using again, recalibrate any expansion pressure device which has been used with materials which have developed such extreme pressure as to leave a permanent set in the spring steel bar. A dial reading at the end of the 16- to 20-hour test period of over 0.01 inch (one turn around the dial) is generally considered to indicate that the steel bar has been subjected to "extreme pressure," and recalibration is required before again using the device.

d. Exercise caution when turning the table up with the specimen in place and engaging the spring steel bar with the rod on the perforated brass plate. If too much force is applied, a temporary set will be placed in the bar which will slowly relieve itself during the 16- to 20-hour soaking period, and result in erroneous deflection readings.

e. Do not, under any circumstances, leave a test specimen unconfined by the expansion pressure device with the layer of free water existing on the specimen in the mold. This is particularly serious with expansive clays and silts, since this condition permits the specimen to expand freely taking up excess water and disrupting the density. The net result will be the unjustifiable reduction of the stabilometer R-value.

F. Determination of the Stabilometer Resistance (R) Value*

10.19 GENERAL

This test method provides a rapid means for determining a measure of the stability or resistance to plastic deformation of compacted materials by means of the previously mentioned Hveem stabilometer. This test is

---

* See AASHO Designation: T 175.

designed to predict the performance of treated or untreated soils used as subgrade, subbases, or base materials for highways. The stabilometer as shown in Figure X-7 is a triaxial type testing device consisting of a rubber sleeve in a metal cylinder with a liquid between the sleeve and cylinder wall. As a vertical load is applied to a specimen, any lateral deformation of the specimen causes a horizontal pressure to be transferred to the liquid and is registered on the horizontal pressure gauge.

10.20 EQUIPMENT

The equipment required for the determination of the resistance (R) value is as follows:

a. Hveem Stabilometer* and accessories as shown in Figure X-7.

b. *Compression Testing Machine:* Minimum capacity of 10,000 pounds.

c. *Metal Cylinder:* Hollow, 4-inch outside diameter x 6 inches high, for calibration purposes.

d. *Metal Follower:* 4-inch outside diameter x 3½ inches high.

10.21 ADJUSTMENT OF APPARATUS

a. Adjust the bronze nut on the stabilometer base so that the distance from the top of the exposed rubber sleeve to the base is 2.4 inches.

b. Adjust the testing machine so that the base plate moves upward at a rate of 0.05 inch per minute. The hydraulic testing machine must be run several minutes before the oil warms sufficiently to maintain a constant speed.

c. Put the metal calibration cylinder in place in the stabilometer. Seat it firmly on the stage and by holding it in place with either the hand or a con-

* Available from Harold F. Smith Tool and Die Shop, 2110 Rassy Way, Sacramento, California 95821.

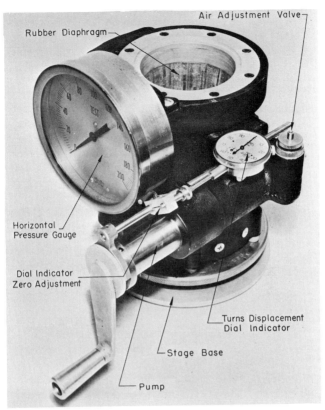

Figure X-7—Stabilometer—Courtesy, California Division of Highways

fining load of 100 pounds in the testing machine, turn the pump to a pressure of exactly 5 psi. Adjust the turns indicator dial to zero. Turn the pump handle at an approximate rate of two turns per second until the stabilometer dial reads 100 psi. The turns indicator dial should read 2.00 ± .05 turns. If it does not, the air in the cell must be adjusted. Remove or add air by means of the valve and the rubber bulb, and repeat the displacement measurement after each air change until the proper number of turns is obtained. Release horizontal pressure, and remove the metal calibration cylinder. The stabilometer is now ready for testing specimens.

10.22 PROCEDURE FOR TESTING

a. Force the specimen which has previously been tested for expansion pressure into the stabilometer. Place the follower on top of the specimen and center the stabilometer assembly under the testing machine head. Lower the testing machine head until it just engages the follower but does not apply any load to the specimen. Adjust the stabilometer pump to give a horizontal pressure of exactly 5 psi. Begin application of a vertical load to the test specimen at a speed of 0.05 inch per minute.

b. Record the stabilometer gauge readings when the vertical pressures are 80 and 160 psi (applied vertical total loads of 1,000 and 2,000 pounds, respectively).

c. Vertical loading by the testing machine must cease at 2,000 pounds, and the load must be immediately reduced to 1,000 pounds. Turn the stabilometer pump so that the horizontal pressure is reduced to 5 psi. This will result in a further reduction in the applied testing machine load, which is normal and should be ignored. Set the turns displacement dial indicator to zero. Turn the pump handle at approximately two turns per second until the stabilometer gauge reads 100 psi. During this operation the applied testing machine load will increase and in some cases exceed the initial 1,000-pound load. As before, these changes in testing machine loadings are normal and should be ignored.

d. Record the number of turns indicated on the dial as the displacement of the specimen. The turns indicator dial reads in increments of 0.001 inch and each 0.10 inch is equal to one turn. Thus, a net reading of 0.250 inch indicates that 2.50 turns were made with the displacement pump. This measurement is known as the turns displacement of the specimen.

e. Calculate the stabilometer R-value from the following formula:

$$R = 100 - \frac{100}{\dfrac{2.5}{D} \left(\dfrac{Pv}{Ph} - 1 \right) + 1}$$

where:

Pv = 160 psi vertical pressure

D = Turns displacement reading

Ph = Horizontal pressure (stabilometer gauge reading for 160 psi vertical pressure)

f. The stabilometer R-value chart (Figure X-8) is normally used to solve the formula in e above.

g. Test specimens should be made having an over-all height of 2.4 inches to 2.6 inches. If this is not possible, the stabilometer stage height should be adjusted and the R-value corrected according to Figure X-9.

10.23 PRECAUTIONS

a. Care must be exercised to avoid disrupting the compacted specimen while transferring it from the mold to the stabilometer. This applies particularly to those samples composed of coarse granular materials.

b. Hydraulic testing machines must be operated several minutes before the oil warms sufficiently to maintain a constant speed.

c. The operator's attention should not be diverted for any reason during the application of the vertical load to the test specimen. Allowing the testing

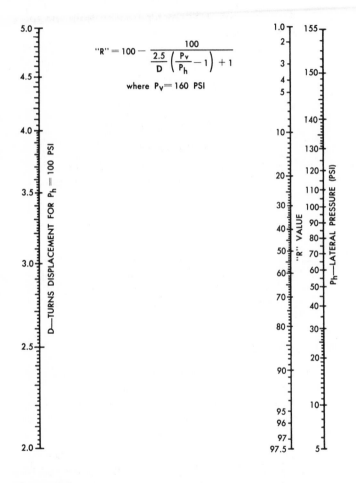

$$"R" = 100 - \frac{100}{\dfrac{2.5}{D}\left(\dfrac{P_v}{P_h} - 1\right) + 1}$$

where $P_v = 160$ PSI

Figure X-8 - CHART FOR DETERMINING "R" VALUE FROM STABILOMETER DATA

machine to load in excess of 2,000 pounds on soft fluid materials can result in damage to the horizontal pressure gauge on the stabilometer.

d. Do not use anything but the fingers to close the air cell needle valve of the stabilometer. The use of pliers or a wrench to tighten it will damage the valve seat and cause it to leak air in subsequent operations.

e. When picking up both the stabilometer and stage base together, make sure that the lock shoe on the bottom of the stabilometer shell is in position to prevent the base from slipping out. The stage weighs about 20 pounds and could cause serious injury if it fell on the operator's foot. It is good practice when carrying the entire assembly to grip it by the bronze adjusting nut on the stage base.

10.24 NOTES

a. The R-values developed by individual test specimens in a group composed of the same material are inverse functions of their moisture contents at compaction.

b. A test specimen which has been destructively disrupted due to rough handling, transfer from the mold to the stabilometer, or as a result of the test itself, will exhibit excessively high horizontal pressure and turns displacement readings.

c. Increasing the roughness or coarseness of the texture on the peripheral surface of a test specimen causes a reduction in the horizontal pressure values obtained from the stabilometer. This influence on the results is brought about by specimen roughness. To compensate for coarse surface texture characteristics, the turns displacement determination is applied through the R-value formula as a correction factor. Soft test specimens also have high displacements. However, these specimens also have high transmitted pressures. It will be noted in the chart for calculating R-values, Figure X-8, that the displacement correction for these materials does not greatly affect the calculated R-value.

10.25 RECORDS OF TEST DATA

a. A sample test data sheet is shown as Figure X-10. This sheet should contain all pertinent data concerning the preparation, compaction, density, exudation, and expansion pressure of test specimens. These data are normally transferred from individual test tickets to the appropriate spaces on the data sheet. The following is a brief discussion relative to the use of a portion of the data sheet.

b. Line 1: A through H represent separate test specimens, and each is fabricated with a different moisture content. For ease of plotting and interpretation, enter the test data for the specimen showing the largest exudation pressure under A, and enter the test data for other specimens in descending order of exudation pressure under B, C, etc.

c. Line 2: The date tested is normally recorded as the date the stabilometer R-value test is completed.

d. Line 3: Enter the compactor air pressure in psi used during the application of the 100 tamps. The normal value for 350 psi foot pressure varies between 21 and 24 pounds. Some clays cannot be compacted at full pressure, and therefore the actual air pressure used should be recorded.

e. Line 4: The initial moisture is determined on a sample weighing at least 200 grams and having the same grading ("as used") as the R-value specimens. The moisture sample is taken during the time the R-value samples are being batched.

f. Line 5: "Water added ml." includes the milliliters of water added for "soaking" plus the final water added during the mixing operation just prior to compaction.

g. Line 7: "Moisture at compaction percent" is the sum of the percent initial moisture and the percent moisture added.

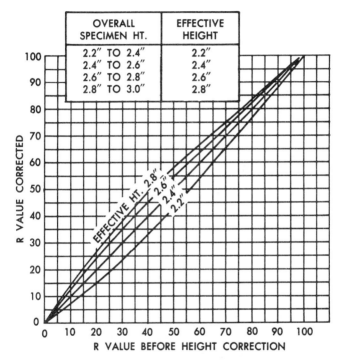

OVERALL SPECIMEN HT.	EFFECTIVE HEIGHT
2.2" TO 2.4"	2.2"
2.4" TO 2.6"	2.4"
2.6" TO 2.8"	2.6"
2.8" TO 3.0"	2.8"

HEIGHT CORRECTION SHOULD BE MADE USING THE TABLE AND CHART ABOVE

EXAMPLE: OVERALL HEIGHT OF 2.74", EFFECTIVE HEIGHT SET AT 2.6" R (UNCORRECTED) = 30; R (CORRECTED) = 35.

Figure X-9—Chart for Correcting "R" Values to Effective Specimen Height of 2.40 Inches

h. Lines 8 and 9: The height of briquette (to 0.01 inch) and the wet weight of briquette in grams are determined prior to the expansion pressure test.

These values are used with the moisture at compaction in the density computations.

i. Lines 11 through 14: The stabilometer data are

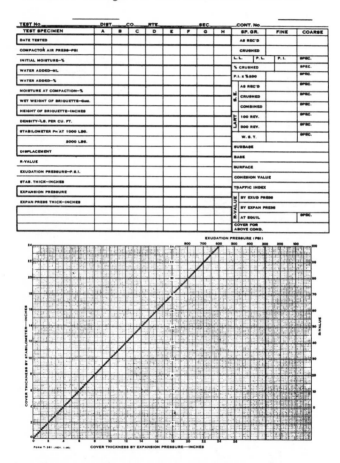

Figure X-10—Sample Data Sheet.

entered as they are determined during the performance of the stabilometer test. The R-value for each specimen is calculated from these data using the alignment chart in Figure X-8.

j. Line 15: The exudation pressure is recorded as the compressive stress in psi at which moisture is extruded from the specimen as indicated by the exudation pressure device.

k. Line 16: The thickness indicated by the stabilometer is determined on the design chart from the R-value for each specimen and recorded.

l. Line 17: In the space provided for expansion pressure, the deflection measurement of the calibrated bar in the expansion pressure device multiplied by 10,000 is entered, and it is called the "dial reading."

10.26 DESIGN R-VALUE

Thickness design of pavements is beyond the scope of this manual. The R-value used for design, however, cannot be determined without the use of a thickness design chart. In the Hveem method the design R-value is found through the use of the work card (Figure X-10) and a thickness design chart in which a traffic index and a unit cohesiometer value are employed, in addition to the R-values from each specimen tested.

So that all test methods described in this manual can use the thickness design chart in The Asphalt Institute Manual Series No. 1, the following method for determining the design R-value is suggested.

Before a design R-value is determined, additional computations must be made using the results of the exudation pressure test, the expansion pressure test, and the stabilometer test. On the design chart (Figure IV-2, Thickness Design Manual, MS-1), determine the "thickness indicated by stabilometer" corresponding to the

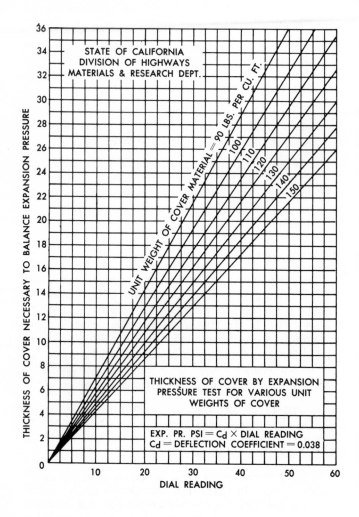

Figure X-11.

R-value for each specimen, and record these data on line 16 of the work card.

The R-value by exudation pressure (300 psi) is interpolated by utilizing the graph provided on the reverse side of the work card, Figure X-10. Plot the thicknesses in inches indicated by the stabilometer for each specimen against the corresponding exudation pressure. Then determine the thickness at the intersection of the curve connecting the points with the 300 psi line, and convert to R-value using the design chart in MS-1

To determine the R-value by expansion pressure, it is first necessary to calculate the thicknesses of cover required by expansion pressure for each specimen from the dial readings recorded on the work card. For design purposes the unit weight of cover is assumed to be 130 pounds per cubic foot. The expansion pressure devices are so calibrated that it is only necessary to divide the dial readings by two to obtain the cover thicknesses on the basis of this assumed weight. If, in special investigations where more accurate information is available, it is desired to use a different weight of cover material, then the cover thicknesses may be determined from the chart in Figure X-11.

The determination of R-value by expansion pressure is accomplished by first plotting thickness indicated by the stabilometer against thickness indicated by expansion pressure on the graph provided on the back of the work card. Then the thickness value at which the curve connecting the points crosses the 45-degree balance line is noted. This thickness is converted to R-value by using the design chart, and the R-value is recorded on the work card.

The R-value at equilibrium (design R-value) is established by taking the lower value of the R-value by exudation and the R-value by expansion.

APPENDICES

APPENDIX A

A.01

Standard Method of Test for

Sieve Analysis of Fine and Coarse Aggregates

AASHO Designation: T 27–60

Scope

1. This method of test covers a procedure for the determination of the particle size distribution of fine and coarse aggregates, using sieves with square openings. The method is also applicable to the use of laboratory screens with round openings. It is not intended for use in the sieve analysis of aggregates recovered from bituminous mixtures or for the sieve analysis of mineral fillers.

Apparatus

2. The apparatus shall consist of the following:

(a) *Balance.*—The balance or scale shall be sensitive to within 0.1 per cent of the weight of the sample to be tested.

(b) *Sieves.*—The sieves with square openings shall be mounted on substantial frames constructed in a manner that will prevent loss of material during sieving. Suitable sieve sizes shall be selected to furnish the information required by the specifications covering the material to be tested. The woven wire cloth sieves shall conform to the Standard Specifications for Sieves for Testing Purposes (AASHO Designation: M 92).

NOTE: If round-hole perforated plate screens are used, the openings shall conform to the applicable dimensions and tolerances prescribed in the Standard Specifications for Sieves for Testing Purposes (AASHO Designation: M 92).

(c) *Oven.*—The oven shall be capable of maintaining a uniform temperature of 110 C (230 F).

Samples

3. (a) Samples for sieve analysis shall be obtained from the materials to be tested by the use of a sample splitter or by the method of quartering. Fine aggregate sampled by the quartering method shall be thoroughly mixed and in a moist condition. The sample for test shall be approximately of the weight desired and shall be the end result of the sampling method. The selection of samples of an exact predetermined weight shall not be attempted.

(b) Samples of fine aggregate for sieve analysis shall weigh, after drying, approximately the amount indicated in the following table:

Material with at least 95 per cent finer than a No 8 (2380-micron) sieve ....100 g.

Material with at least 90 per cent finer than a No. 4 (4760-micron) sieve and more than 5 per cent coarser than a No. 8 sieve ....500 g.

In no case, however, shall the fraction retained on any sieve at the completion of the sieving operation weigh more than 4 g. per sq. in. of sieving surface (Note).

NOTE: This amounts to 200 g. for the usual 8-in. diameter sieve. The amount of material retained on the critical sieve may be regulated by: *(1)* the introduction of a sieve having larger openings than in the critical sieve or, *(2)* by the proper selection of the size of the sample.

(c) Samples of coarse aggregate for sieve analysis shall weigh, after drying, not less than an amount indicated in the following table:

Nominal Maximum Size of Particle, in.	Minimum Weight of Sample, g.[1]
⅜	1 000
½	2 500
¾	5 000
1	10 000
1½	15 000
2	20 000
2½	25 000
3	30 000
3½	35 000

[1] For samples weighing 5000 g. or more it is recommended that sieves mounted in frames 16 in. in diameter or larger be used.

(*d*) In the case of mixtures of fine and coarse aggregates, the material shall be separated into two sizes on the No. 4 (4760-micron) sieve and the samples of fine and coarse aggregates shall be prepared in accordance with Paragraphs (*b*) and (*c*).

(*e*) In the case of fine aggregate, the material finer than the No. 200 (74-micron) sieve shall be determined in accordance with the Standard Method of Test for Amount of Material Finer than No. 200 Sieve in Aggregates (AAS HO Designation: T 11) and the sieve analysis made on the material coarser than the No. 200 (74-micron) sieve.

Preparation of Sample

4. Samples shall first be subjected to the Standard Method of Test for Material Finer Than the No. 200 Sieve in Aggregate by Washing, AASHO Method T 11. This procedure may be omitted provided the total amount of material finer than the No. 200 sieve is not required and provided the accuracy requirements for the sieve analysis do not require washing of the particles. All samples shall be dried to substantially constant weight at a temperature not exceeding 110 C (230 F).

Procedure

5. (*a*) The sample shall be separated into a series of sizes using such sieves as are necessary to determine compliance with the specifications for the material under test. The sieving operation shall be conducted by means of a lateral and vertical motion of the sieve, accompanied by jarring action so as to keep the sample moving continuously over the surface of the sieve. In no case shall fragments in the sample be turned or manipulated through the sieve by hand. Sieving shall be continued until not more than 1 per cent by weight of the residue passes any sieve during 1 min. On that portion of the sample retained on the No. 4 (4760-micron) sieve, the above described procedure for determining thoroughness of sieving shall be carried out with a single layer of material. When mechanical sieving is used the thoroughness of sieving shall be tested by using the hand method of sieving as described above.

(*b*) The weight of each size shall be determined on a scale or balance conforming to the requirements specified in Section 2 (*a*). If the total amount of material finer than the No. 200 sieve is desired it shall be determined by adding the weight of material passing the No. 200 sieve by dry sieving to that lost by washing as determined with the use of AASHO Method T 11.

Report

6. The results of the sieve analysis shall be reported as follows: (*a*) total percentages passing each sieve, or (*b*) total percentages retained on each sieve, or (*c*) percentages retained between consecutive sieves, depending upon the form of the specifications for the use of the material under test. Percentages shall be reported to the nearest whole number, except the percentage passing the No. 200 sieve shall be reported to the nearest 0.1 percent. Percentages shall be calculated on the basis of the total weight of the sample including any material finer than the No. 200 sieve.

——————— o ———————

Standard Methods of

Mechanical Analysis of Soils

AASHO Designation: T 88–57

Scope

1. This method describes a procedure for the quantitative determination of the distribution of particles sizes in soils.

Apparatus

2. The apparatus shall consist of the following:

(a) Balance.—A balance sensitive to 0.1 gm. for weighing small samples; for large samples, the balance is to be sensitive to within 0.1 percent of the weight of the sample to be tested.

(b) Stirring Apparatus.—A mechanically operated stirring apparatus consisting of an electric motor suitably mounted to turn a vertical shaft at a speed not less than 10,000 revolutions per minute without load, a replaceable stirring paddle made of metal, plastic or hard rubber similar to the design shown in Figure 1, and a dispersion cup conforming to either of the designs shown in Figure 2.

(Alternate b) Dispersing Device.—An air-jet type dispersing device similar to either of the designs shown in Figure 3.

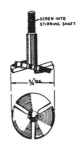

FIG. 1.—*Detail of Stirring Paddle*

(c) Hydrometer.—A hydrometer of the exact size and shape shown in figure 4, the body of which has been blown in a mold to assure duplication of all dimensions, and equipped with either scale A or scale B. Scale A shall be graduated from —5 to + 60 grams of soil per liter, and hydrometers equipped with this scale shall be identified as 152 H. It shall be calibrated on the assumption that distilled water has a specific gravity of 1.000 at 68 F. and that the soil in suspension has a specific gravity of 2.65. Scale B shall be graduated from 0.995 to 1.038 specific gravity and calibrated to read 1.000 in distilled water at 68 F. (20.0 C.). Hydrometers equipped with this scale shall be identified as 151 H.

(d) A glass graduate 18 inches in height and 2½ inches in diameter, and graduated for a volume of 1000 ml.

(e) Thermometer. — A Fahrenheit thermometer accurate to 1 F. (0.5 C).

(f) Sieves.—A series of sieves of square mesh woven wire cloth, conforming to the requirements of Standard Specifications for Sieves for Testing Purposes (A.A.S.H.O. Designation: M 92). The sieves required are as follows:

```
         2-inch sieve
       1½-inch sieve
         1-inch sieve
        ¾-inch sieve
        ⅜-inch sieve
No.      4 sieve
No.     10 sieve
No.     40 sieve
No.    200 sieve
```

(g) Water Bath or Constant Temperature Room.—A water bath or constant temperature room for maintaining the soil suspension at a constant temperature during the hydrometer analysis. A satisfactory water bath is an insulated tank which maintains the suspension at a convenient constant temperature as near 68 F. (20.0 C) as the

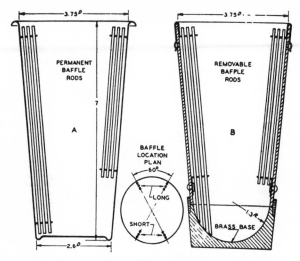

FIG. 2.—*Dispersion Cups.*

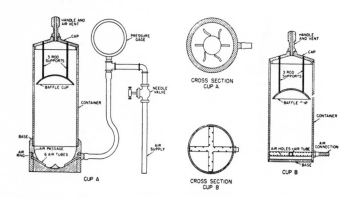

FIG. 3.—*The Wintermyer Soil Dispersion Cups.*

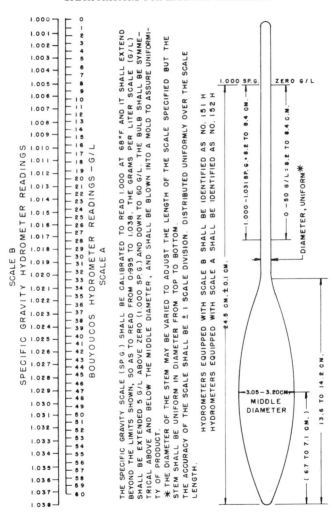

FIG. 4.—*Hydrometer.*

room and faucet-water temperature will permit. Such a device is illustrated in Figure 5. In cases where the work is performed in a room at an automatically controlled constant temperature, the water bath is not necessary and subsequent reference to a constant temperature bath shall be interpreted as meaning either a water bath or a constant temperature room.

(h) Beaker.—A beaker of 250-ml. capacity.

Sample

3. The samples required for this test shall include all of the material on the No. 10 (2,000 micron) sieve, plus a 60- or 110-gm. representative portion of the fraction passing the No. 10 sieve, the larger quantity being required only when this fraction is very sandy. These samples shall be obtained in accordance with the Standard Method of Dry Preparation of Disturbed Soil Samples for Test (AASHO Designation: T 87), or the Standard Method of Wet Preparation of Disturbed Soil Samples for Test (AASHO Designation: T 146).

Sieve Analysis of Fraction Retained on No. 10 Sieve

4. *(a)* The portion of the sample retained on the No. 10 sieve shall be separated into a series of sizes by the use of the 2-inch, 1½-inch, 1-inch, ¾-inch, ⅜-inch, and the No. 4 sieve.

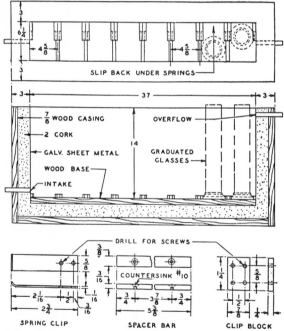

Fig 5.—*Tank for Maintaining Soil Suspension at Constant Temperature During Hydrometer Analysis.*

(b) The sieving operation shall be conducted by means of a lateral and vertical motion of the sieve, accompanied by jarring action so as to keep the sample moving continuously over the surface of the sieve. In no case shall fragments in the sample be turned or manipulated through the sieve by hand. Sieving shall be continued until not more than 1 percent by weight of the residue passes any sieve during 1 minute. When sieving machines are used, their thoroughness of sieving shall be tested by comparison with hand methods of sieving as above described.

(c) The portion of the sample retained on each sieve shall be weighed and the weight recorded although it shall be permissible to record the accumulated weights as the contents of each successive sieve is added to the fractions previously deposited on the scales pan.

HYDROMETER AND SIEVE ANALYSIS OF FRACTION PASSING THE NO. 10 SIEVE
Hygroscopic Moisture
5. A 10-gm. portion of the fraction of the sample passing the No. 10 sieve shall be used for the determination of the hygroscopic moisture. This portion of the sample shall be weighed, dried to constant weight in an oven at 110 C. (230 F.), weighed, and the results recorded.

Dispersion of Soil Sample
6. Approximately 50 grams of most soils or 100 grams of very sandy soils shall be taken from the fraction passing the No. 10 sieve by use of a riffle sampler, weighed, placed in a 250-ml. beaker, covered with 125 ml. of stock solution of the selected dispersing agent, stirred thoroughly with a glass rod, and allowed to soak for a minimum of 12 hours. Any of the four dispersing agents listed in Table 1 may be used.

The stock solution shall be prepared by dissolving the quantity of the salt given in the table in sufficient distilled water to make a liter of solution. After soaking, the contents of the beaker shall be washed into one of the dispersion cups shown in Figure 2, distilled water added until the cup is more than half full, and the contents dispersed for a period of 1 minute in the mechanical stirring apparatus.

Alternate Method for Dispersion
7. *(a)* The representative soil sample shall be weighed and placed in a 250-ml. beaker, covered with 125 ml. of the stock solution of the selected dispersing agent specified in Section 6, and allowed to soak for a minimum of 12 hours.

(b) The air-jet dispersion apparatus shall be assembled as shown in Fig. 3 without the cover cap in place. The needle valve controlling the line pressure shall be opened until the pressure gauge indicates one pound per square inch air pressure. This initial air pressure is required to prevent the soil-water mixture from entering the air-jet chamber when the mixture is transferred to the dispersion cup. After the apparatus is adjusted, the soil-water mixture shall be transferred from the beaker to the dispersion cup, using a wash bottle to assist in the transfer operation.

(c) The volume of the soil-water mixture in the dispersion cup shall not exceed 250 ml. The cover containing the baffle plate shall be placed upon the dispersion cup and the needle valve opened until the pressure gauge reads 20 pounds per square inch. The soil-water mixture shall be dispersed for 5, 10, or 15 minutes depending upon the plasticity index of the soil. Soils with a PI of 5 or less shall be dispersed for 5 minutes; soils with a PI between 6 and 20 for 10 minutes; and soils with a PI greater than 20 for 15 minutes. Soils containing large percentages of

TABLE I.—DISPERSING AGENTS

Chemical	Grams of salt per liter of stock solution	Formula
Sodium hexametaphosphate buffered with sodium carbonate[1]	45.7	$NaPO_3$ or $(NaPO_3)_6$
Sodium polyphos	21.6	$Na_{12}P_{10}O_{31}$
Sodium tripolyphosphate	18.8	$Na_5P_3O_{10}$
Sodium tetraphosphate[2]	35.1	$Na_6P_4O_{13}$

[1] Marketed as "Calgon."
[2] Marketed as "Quadrofos."

mica need be dispersed for 1 minute only.

(d) After the dispersion period is completed, the needle valve shall be closed until the pressure gauge indicates one pound per square inch. The cover shall be removed and all adhering soil particles washed back into the dispersion cup. The soil water suspension shall then be washed into the 1000-ml. glass graduate and the needle valve closed.

Hydrometer Test

8. (a) After dispersion, the mixture shall be transferred to the glass graduate and distilled water having the same temperature as the constant temperature bath added until the mixture attains a volume of 1000 ml. The graduate containing the soil suspension shall then be placed in the constant temperature bath. When the soil suspension attains the temperature of the bath, the graduate shall be removed and its contents thoroughly shaken for 1 minute, the palm of the hand being used as a stopper over the mouth of the graduate.

(b) At the conclusion of this shaking, the time shall be recorded, the graduate placed in the bath, and readings taken with the hydrometer at the end of 2 minutes. The hydrometer shall be read at the top of the meniscus formed by the suspension around its stem. If hydrometer with scale A is used, it shall be read to the nearest 0.5 gm. per liter. Scale B shall be read to the nearest 0.0005 specific gravity. Subsequent readings shall be taken at intervals of 5, 15, 30, 60, 250 and 1440 minutes after the beginning of sedimentation. Readings of the thermometer placed in the soil suspension shall be made immediately following each hydrometer reading and recorded.

(c) After each reading the hydrometer shall be very carefully removed from the soil suspension and placed with a spinning motion in a graduate of clean water. About 25 or 30 seconds before the time for a reading, it shall be taken from the clear water, and slowly immersed in the soil suspension to assure that it comes to rest before the appointed reading time.

Sieve Analysis

9. At the conclusion of the final read-

ing of the hydrometer, the suspension shall be washed on a No. 200 (74 micron) sieve. That fraction retained on the No. 200 sieve shall be dried and a sieve analysis made, using the following sieves: No. 40, No. 60, and No. 200.

CALCULATIONS

Percentage of Hygroscopic Moisture

10. The hygroscopic moisture shall be expressed as a percentage of the weight of the oven-dried soil and shall be determined as follows:

$$\text{Percentage of hygroscopic moisture} = \frac{w - w_1}{w_1} \times 100$$

where:

w = weight of air-dried soil, and
w_1 = weight of oven-dried soil

To correct the weight of the air-dried sample for hygroscopic moisture, the given value shall be multiplied by the expression:

$$\frac{100}{100 + \text{per centage of hygroscopic moisture}}$$

Coarse Material

11. (a) The percentage of coarse material shall be calculated from the weights of the fractions recorded during the sieving of the material retained on the No. 10 sieve, in accordance with Section 4, and the total weights recorded during the preparation of the sample, in accordance with the Standard Method of Dry Preparation of Disturbed Samples for Tests (A.A.S.H.O. Designation: T 87).

(b) The percentage of coarse material retained on the No. 10 sieve shall be calculated as follows: From the weight of the air-dried total sample, subtract the weight of the oven-dried fraction retained on the No. 10 sieve. The difference is assumed to equal the weight of the air-dried fraction passing the No. 10 sieve (Note 1).

NOTE 1: According to this assumption, no hygroscopic moisture is contained in the air-dried particles retained on the No. 10 sieve, when as a matter of fact a small percentage of moisture may be present in this fraction. This amount of moisture, compared with that held in the pores of the fraction passing the No. 10 sieve, is relatively small. Therefore, any error produced by the assumption as stated may be considered negligible in amount.

The weight of the fraction passing the No. 10 sieve shall be corrected for hygroscopic moisture as indicated in Section 10. To this value shall be added the weight of the oven-dried fraction retained on the No. 10 sieve to obtain the weight of the total test sample corrected for hygroscopic moisture. The fractions retained on the No. 10 and coarser sieves shall be expressed as percentages of this corrected weight.

Percentage of Soil in Suspension

12. (a) Hydrometer readings made at temperatures other than 68 F. shall be corrected by applying the appropriate composite correction from one of the following tables. Tables 151 H and 152 H list composite corrections for hydrometers 151 H and 152 H to account for the different dispersing agents, tempera-

ture variations from 68 F, (20.0 C.), and height of the meniscus on the stem of the hydrometer.

(b) The percentage of the dispersed soil in suspension represented by different corrected hydrometer readings depends upon both the amount and the specific gravity of the soil dispersed. The percentage of dispersed soil remaining in suspension shall be calculated as follows:

For hydrometer 152 H

$$P = \frac{Ra}{w} \times 100$$

For hydrometer 151 H

$$P = \frac{1606(R-1)a}{w} \times 100$$

TABLE 151 H.—COMPOSITE CORRECTIONS to be applied to readings of AASHO standard soil hydrometers No. 151 H at the temperatures and in dispersing solutions[1] indicated, to convert to readings at 20 C (68 F) in distilled water.

Temperature of solution	Correction of hydrometer reading for dispersing agent indicated			
	Na PO₃	Na₁₃P₁₀O₃₁	Na₄P₂O₁₀	Na₄P₄O₁₃
Degrees C	Sp. G	Sp. G	Sp. G	Sp. G
19	− .00456	− .00214	− .00214	− .00342
19½	− .00443	− .00204	− .00204	− .00330
20	− .00430	− .00193	− .00193	− .00318
20½	− .00418	− .00183	− .00183	− .00308
21	− .00404	− .00173	− .00173	− .00298
21½	− .00392	− .00162	− .00162	− .00286
22	− .00379	− .00151	− .00151	− .00276
22½	− .00367	− .00141	− .00141	− .00265
23	− .00354	− .00131	− .00131	− .00254
23½	− .00342	− .00120	− .00120	− .00243
24	− .00329	− .00110	− .00110	− .00232
24½	− .00316	− .00100	− .00100	− .00222
25	− .00304	− .00089	− .00089	− .00211
25½	− .00292	− .00079	− .00079	− .00200
26	− .00280	− .00068	− .00068	− .00190
26½	− .00267	− .00058	− .00058	− .00179
27	− .00255	− .00047	− .00047	− .00168
27½	− .00244	− .00037	− .00037	− .00158
28	− .00232	− .00027	− .00027	− .00148
28½	− .00220	− .00017	− .00017	− .00137
29	− .00207	− .00006	− .00006	− .00125
29½	− .00195	+ .00004	+ .00004	− .00115
30	− .00184	+ .00014	+ .00014	− .00106
30½	− .00171	+ .00025	+ .00025	− .00094
31	− .00158	+ .00035	+ .00035	− .00083
31½	− .00146	+ .00046	+ .00046	− .00073
32	− .00184	+ .00057	+ .00057	− .00062
32½	− .00122	+ .00068	+ .00068	− .00051
33	− .00110	+ .00079	+ .00079	− .00040
33½	− .00097	+ .00089	+ .00089	− .00030
34	− .00085	+ .00099	+ .00099	− .00019
34½	− .00073	+ .00110	+ .00110	− .00009
35	− .00061	+ .00121	+ .00121	+ .00002

[1] Solutions are composed of 125 ml. of stock solution prescribed in Sec. 6 diluted to make 1000 ml. of final solution.

where:

P = percentage of originally dispersed soil remaining in suspension.

R = corrected hydrometer reading.

w = weight in grams of soil originally dispersed minus the hygroscopic moisture, and

a = constant depending on the density of the suspension.

For an assumed value of G for the specific gravity of the soil, and a water density of 1.000 at 68 F. (20.0 C.), the value of "a" may be obtained by the formula:

$$a = \frac{2.6500 - 1.000}{2.6500} \times \frac{G}{G - 1.000}$$

The values of "a", given to two decimal places are shown in table 2.

TABLE 2.—VALUES OF a, FOR DIFFERENT SPECIFIC GRAVITIES

Specific Gravity, G	Constant, a
2.95	0.94
2.85	0.96
2.75	0.98
2.65	1.00
2.55	1.02
2.45	1.05
2.35	1.08

TABLE 152H.—COMPOSITE CORRECTIONS to be applied to readings of AASHO standard soil hydrometers No. 152H at the temperatures and in dispersing solutions[1] indicated, to convert to readings at 68 F (20 C) in distilled water.

Temperature of solution	Correction of hydrometer reading for dispersing agent indicated			
	Na PO₃	Na₁₂P₁₀O₃₁	Na₄P₂O₁₀	Na₄P₄O₁₃
Degrees F	Gm./L	Gm./L	Gm./L	Gm./L
66	−7.4	−3.5	−3.5	−5.5
67	−7.2	−3.3	−3.3	−5.3
68	−6.9	−3.1	−3.1	−5.1
69	−6.7	−2.9	−2.9	−4.9
70	−6.5	−2.7	−2.7	−4.7
71	−6.3	−2.6	−2.6	−4.6
72	−6.1	−2.4	−2.4	−4.4
73	−5.8	−2.2	−2.2	−4.2
74	−5.6	−2.0	−2.0	−4.0
75	−5.4	−1.8	−1.8	−3.8
76	−5.2	−1.6	−1.6	−3.6
77	−4.9	−1.4	−1.4	−3.4
78	−4.7	−1.2	−1.2	−3.2
79	−4.5	−1.1	−1.1	−3.0
80	−4.3	−0.9	−0.9	−2.8
81	−4.1	−0.7	−0.7	−2.6
82	−3.8	−0.5	−0.5	−2.4
83	−3.6	−0.3	−0.3	−2.2
84	−3.4	−0.1	−0.1	−2.1
85	−3.2	+0.1	+0.1	−1.9
86	−3.0	+0.2	+0.2	−1.7
87	−2.7	+0.4	+0.4	−1.5
88	−2.5	+0.6	+0.6	−1.3
89	−2.3	+0.8	+0.8	−1.1
90	−2.1	+1.0	+1.0	−0.9
91	−1.9	+1.2	+1.2	−0.7
92	−1.7	+1.4	+1.4	−0.5
93	−1.4	+1.6	+1.6	−0.4
94	−1.2	+1.8	+1.8	−0.2
95	−1.0	+2.0	+2.0	0.0
96	−0.8	+2.1	+2.1	+0.2
97	−0.6	+2.3	+2.3	+0.4
98	−0.4	+2.5	+2.5	+0.6

[1] Solutions are composed of 125 ml. of stock solution prescribed in Sec. 6 diluted to make 1000 ml. of final solution.

It is sufficiently accurate for ordinary tests to select the constant for the specific gravity nearest to that of the particular soil tested.

(c) To convert the percentages of soil in suspension to percentages of the total test sample including the fraction retained on the No. 10 sieve, the percentage of originally dispersed soil remaining in suspension shall be multiplied by the expression

$$\frac{100 - \text{percentage retained on No. 10 sieve}}{100}$$

Diameter of Soil Particles in Suspension

13. (a) The maximum diameter, d, of the particles in suspension, corresponding to the percentage indicated by a given hydrometer reading, shall be calculated by the use of Stokes' Law.

According to Stokes law:

$$d = \sqrt{\frac{30 \, nL}{980(G - G_1)T}}$$

where:

d = maximum grain diameter in millimeters.

n = coefficient of viscosity of the suspending medium (in this case water) in poises. Varies with changes in temperature of the suspending medium.

L = distance in cm. through which soil particles settle in a given period of time.

T = time in minutes, period of sedimentation.

G = specific gravity of soil particles, and

G_1 = specific gravity of the suspending medium (approximately 1.0 for water).

(b) The maximum grain diameter in suspension for assumed conditions and corresponding to the periods of sedimentation specified in this procedure are given in Table 3. These grain diameters shall be corrected for the conditions of test by applying the proper correction factors as described and explained below.

TABLE 3.—MAXIMUM GRAIN DIAMETER IN SUSPENSION UNDER ASSUMED CONDITIONS

Time	Max. Grain Diameter
Min.	Mm.
2	.040
5	.026
15	.015
30	.010
60	.0074
250	.0036
1,440	.0015

(c) The grain diameters given in Table 3 are calculated according to the following assumptions:

L, the distance through which the particles fall is constant and equal to 17.5 cm.

n, the coefficient of viscosity equals 0.01005 pois, that of water at 68 F.

G, the specific gravity of the soil is constant and equal to 2.65.

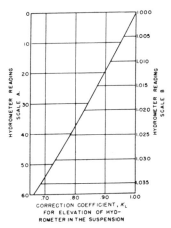

FIG. 6.—Correction Factor K_L

(d) The grain diameters corrected for other than the assumed conditions shall be obtained by the formula

$$d = d' \times K_L \times K_G \times K_s$$

wherein:

d = corrected grain diameter in mm.

d' = grain diameter obtained from table 2.

K_L = correction factor obtained from figure 6 when the hydrometer reading not adjusted for composite correction is used for the ordinate reading.

K_G = correction factor obtained from figure 7A.

K_s = correction factor obtained from figure 7B.

(e) The coefficient K_G and K_s are independent of the shape and position of the hydrometer and are as shown in Figures 7A and 7B.

Fine Sieve Analysis

14. (a) The percentage of the dispersed soil sample retained on each of the sieves in the sieve analysis of the

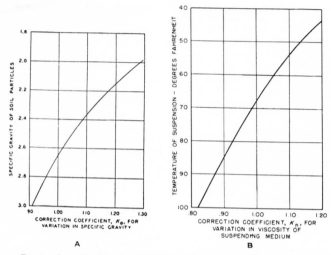

Fig. 7.—*Grain Diameter Correction Curves for Variation in Specific Gravity of Soil and in Viscosity of Suspending Medium.*

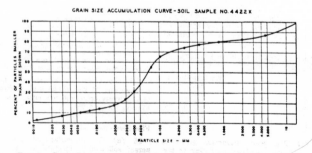

Fig. 8.—*Grain Diameter Accumulation Curve for Soil Sample No. 4422X.*

material washed on the No. 200 shall be obtained by dividing the weight of fraction retained on each sieve by the oven-dry weight of the dispersed soil and multiplying by 100.

(b) The percentages of the total test sample, including the fraction retained on the No. 10 (2000-micron) sieve, shall be obtained by multiplying these values by the expression:

$$\frac{100 \text{ minus the percentage retained on No. 10 sieve}}{100}$$

Plotting

15. The accumulated percentages of grains of different diameters shall be plotted on semilogarithmic paper to obtain a "grain size accumulation curve," such as that shown in Fig. 8.

Report

16. *(a)* The results, read from the accumulation curve, shall be reported as follows:

(a) Particles larger than 2 mm.............per cent
(b) Coarse sand, 2.0 to 0.42 mm...........per cent
(c) Fine sand, 0.42 to 0.074 mm...........per cent
(d) Silt, 0.074 to 0.005 mm...............per cent
(e) Clay, smaller than 0.005 mm...........per cent
(f) Colloids, smaller than 0.001 mm......per cent

(b) The results of complete mechanical analyses furnished by the combined sieve and hydrometer analyses shall be reported as follows:

SIEVE ANALYSIS

Sieve Size	Per cent Passing
¾-inch	....
1½-inch	....
1-inch	....
¾-inch	....
½-inch	....
No. 4	....
No. 10	....
No. 40	....
No. 200	....

HYDROMETER ANALYSIS

Smaller Than	Per cent
.02 mm.	....
.005 mm.	....
.001 mm.	....

For materials examined for any particular type of work or purpose, only such fractions shall be reported as are included in the specifications or other requirements for the work or purpose.

Standard Methods of

Determining the Liquid Limit of Soils

AASHO Designation: T 89–60

Definition

1. The liquid limit of a soil is that water content as determined in accordance with the following procedure at which the soil passes from a plastic to a liquid state.

Apparatus

2. The apparatus shall consist of the following:

(a) Evaporating Dish.—A porcelain evaporating dish about 4½ in. in diameter.

(b) Spatula.—A spatula or pill knife having a blade about 3 in. in length and about ¾ in. in width.

(c) Liquid Limit Device.—A mechanical device consisting of a brass dish and carriage, constructed according to the plan and dimensions shown in Fig. 1.

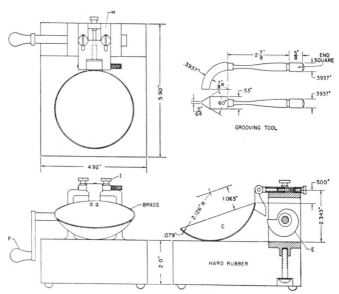

Fig. 1.—*Mechanical Liquid Limit Device.*

(d) Grooving Tool. — A combined grooving tool and gage conforming to the dimensions shown in Fig. 1.

(e) Containers. — Suitable containers such as matched watch glasses which will prevent loss of moisture during weighing.

(f) Balance.—A balance sensitive to 0.1 g.

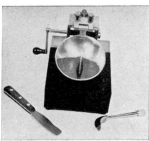

FIG. 1A.—*Liquid limit device with soil sample in place.*

MECHANICAL METHOD

Sample

3. A sample weighing about 50 g. shall be taken from the thoroughly mixed portion of the material passing the No. 40 (420-micron) sieve which has been obtained in accordance with the Standard Method of Preparing Disturbed Soil Samples (AASHO Designation: T 87), or the Standard Method of Wet Preparation of Disturbed Soil Samples for Test (AASHO Designation: T 146).

Adjustment of Mechanical Device

4. *(a)* The liquid limit device shall be inspected to determine that the device is in good working order; that the pin connecting the cup is not worn sufficiently to permit side play; that the screws connecting the cup to the hanger arm are tight; and that a groove has not been worn in the cup through long usage. The grooving tool shall be inspected to determine that the critical dimensions are as shown in Fig. 1.

(b) By means of the gage on the handle of the grooving tool, and the ad-justment plate H, Fig. 1, the height to which the cup C is lifted shall be adjusted so that the point on the cup which comes in contact with the base is exactly 1 cm. (0.3937 in.) above base. The adjustment plate H shall then be secured by tightening the screws, I. With the gage still in place, the adjustment shall be checked by revolving the crank rapidly several times. If the adjustment is correct a slight ringing sound will be heard when the cam strikes the cam follower. If the cup is raised off the gage or no sound is heard, further adjustment shall be made.

Procedure

5. *(a)* The soil sample shall be placed in the evaporating dish and thoroughly mixed with 15 to 20 cc. of distilled water by alternately and repeatedly stirring, kneading, and chopping with a spatula. Further additions of water shall be made in increments of 1 to 3 cc. Each increament of water shall be thoroughly mixed with the soil as previously described before another increment of water is added. The cup of the liquid limit device should not be used for mixing soil and water.

(b) When sufficient water has been thoroughly mixed with the soil to form a uniform mass of stiff consistency, a sufficient quantity of this mixture shall be placed in the cup above the spot where the cup rests on the base and shall then be squeezed and spread into the position shown in Fig. 1A with as few strokes of the spatula as possible, care being taken to prevent the entrapment of air bubbles within the mass. With the spatula the soil shall be leveled and at the same time trimmed to a depth of 1 cm. at the point of maximum thickness. The excess soil shall be returned to the evaporating dish. The soil in the cup of the mechanical device shall be divided by a firm stroke of the grooving tool along the diameter through the centerline of the cam follower so that a clean, sharp groove of the proper dimensions will be formed. To avoid tearing of the sides of the groove or slipping of the soil cake on the cup, up to six strokes, from front to back or from back to front counting as one stroke, shall be permitted. The depth of the groove should be increased with each

stroke and only the last stroke should scrape the bottom of the cup.

(c) The cup containing the sample prepared as described in (b) shall be lifted and dropped by turning the crank F at the rate of two revolutions per second until the two sides of the sample come in contact at the bottom of the groove along a distance of about ½ inch. The number of shocks required to close the groove this distance shall be recorded. The base of the machine shall not be held with the free hand while the crank F is turned.

(d) A slice of soil approximately the width of the spatula, extending from edge to edge of the soil cake at right angles to the groove and including that portion of the groove in which the soil flowed together, shall be removed and placed in a suitable container. The container and soil shall then be weighed and the weight recorded. The soil in the container shall be oven-dried to constant weight at 110 C. (230 F.) and weighed. This weight shall be recorded and the loss in weight due to drying shall be recorded as the weight of water.

(e) The soil remaining in the cup shall be transferred to the evaporating dish. The cup and grooving tool shall then be washed and dried in preparation for the next trial.

(f) The foregoing operations shall be repeated for at least two additional portions of the sample to which sufficient water has been added to bring the soil to a more fluid condition. The object of this procedure is to obtain samples of such consistency that at least one determination will be made in each of the following ranges of shocks: 25-35, 20-30, 15-25.

Calculation

6. The water content of the soil shall be expressed as the moisture content in percentage of the weight of the oven-dried soil and shall be calculated as follows:

$$\text{Percentage moisture} = \frac{\text{wt. of water}}{\text{wt. of oven-dried soil}} \times 100$$

Preparation of Flow Curve

7. A "flow curve" representing the relation between moisture content and corresponding number of shocks shall be plotted on a semilogarithmic graph with the moisture contents as abscissae on the arithmetical scale, and the number of shocks as ordinates on the logarithmic scale. The flow curve shall be a straight line drawn as nearly as possible through the three or more plotted points.

Liquid Limit

8. The moisture content corresponding to the intersection of the flow curve with the 25 shock ordinate shall be taken as the liquid limit of the soil.

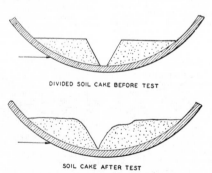

DIVIDED SOIL CAKE BEFORE TEST

SOIL CAKE AFTER TEST

FIG. 2—*Diagram Illustrating Liquid Limit Test.*

MECHANICAL METHOD
(ALTERNATE)

Sample

9. The sample shall be the same as described in Section 3.

Procedure

10. The procedure shall be the same as prescribed in Section 5(a) through 5(e) except that the moisture sample taken in accordance with Section 5(d) shall be taken only for the accepted trial.

(f) At least two groove closures shall be observed before one is accepted for the record, so as to assure that the accepted number of blows is truly characteristic of the soil under test.

Note 1.—Some soils are slow to absorb water, therefore it is possible to add the increments of water so fast that a false liquid limit value is obtained. This can be avoided if more mixing and/or time is allowed.

(g) Groove closures between 15 and 40 blows may be accepted if variations of ± 5 percent of the true liquid limit are tolerable.

(h) For accuracy equal to that obtained by the standard three-point method, the accepted number of blows for groove closure shall be restricted between 22 and 28 blows.

Calculation

11. The water content of the soil at the time of the accepted closure shall be calculated in accordance with Section 6.

Liquid Limit

12. (a) The liquid limit shall be determined by one of the following methods: the nomograph, figure 3; the multi-curve chart, figure 4. the slide-rule with a special "blows" scale, figure 5, or by any other method of calculation that produces equally accurate liquid limit values. The standard three-point method shall be used as a referee test to settle all controversies.

(b) The key in figure 3 illustrates the use of the nomograph (mean slope).

(c) The chart (multi-flow-curve), figure 4, is used by plotting on it a point representing the moisture content vs. number of blows for the accepted trial, and drawing a line through the plotted point parallel to the nearest chart curve. The moisture content corresponding to the intersection of this line with the 25-blow line shall be recorded as the liquid limit.

(d) The special slide-rule, figure 5, is used by setting the hair line of the indicator slide coincident with the A-scale value of the moisture content for the accepted groove closure, and moving the special scale until the number of blows used for closure is also under the hair line. The liquid limit will then be found on the A-scale opposite the end index of the B-scale, or opposite the middle index of the B-scale, which in turn is directly in line with the 25-blow mark of the special scale.

HAND METHOD (Alternate)

Sample

13. A sample weighing about 30 g. shall be taken from the thoroughly mixed portion of the material passing the No. 40 (420-micron) sieve which has been obtained in accordance with the Standard Method of Dry Preparation of Disturbed Soil Samples (A.A.S.H.O. Designation: T 87).

Procedure

14. (a) The air-dried soil shall be placed in the evaporating dish and thoroughly mixed with distilled water until the mass becomes a thick paste. The mass of soil shall then be shaped into a layer 1 cm. (approximately ⅜ in.) in thickness at the center and divided into two portions with the grooving tool, as shown in the illustration at the top of Fig. 2.

(b) The dish shall be held firmly in one hand, with the groove parallel to the line of sight, and tapped lightly with a horizontal motion against the heel of the other hand 10 times. The intensity of the blows shall be such that the effect on the soil sample is equivalent to that produced by 25 shocks applied to a sample of the soil at the same moisture content by dropping the brass cup of the mechanical device through a distance of 1 cm. (0.3937 in.) at the rate of two drops per second.

SPECIFICATIONS FOR HIGHWAY MATERIALS

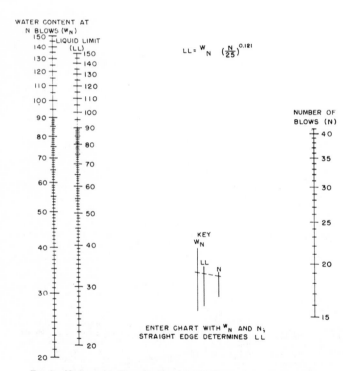

$$LL = W_N \left(\frac{N}{25}\right)^{0.121}$$

KEY

ENTER CHART WITH W_N AND N;
STRAIGHT EDGE DETERMINES LL

FIG. 3.—*Nomographic Chart Developed by the Waterways Experiment Station, Corps of Engineers, U. S. Army, to Determine Liquid Limit Using Mean Slope Method.*

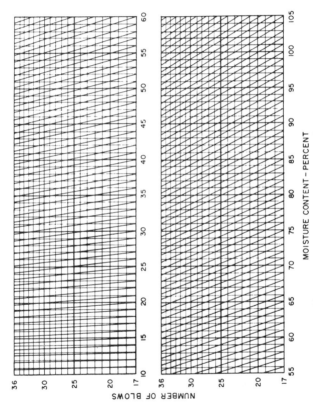

Fig. 4.—Chart Developed by Washington State Highway Department for the Calculation of the Liquid Limit.

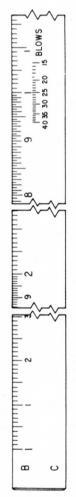

A - LOCATION OF SPECIAL SCALE (BLOWS) WITH RESPECT TO B SCALE OF SLIDE RULE

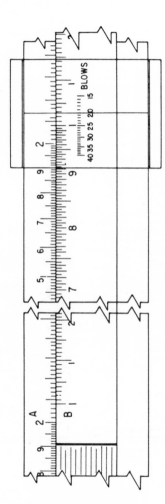

B - SLIDE RULE SET FOR 21.4 PERCENT MOISTURE AT 20 BLOWS, INDICATING CALCULATED LIQUID LIMIT OF 20.8

Fig. 5.—*Slide Rule with Special Scale for the Calculation of Liquid Limit.*

(c) If the lower edges of the two-soil portions do not flow together, as shown at the bottom of Fig. 2, after 10 blows have been struck, the moisture content is below the liquid limit. More water shall be added and the procedure repeated. If the lower edges meet before 10 blows have been struck, the moisture content is above the liquid limit and the soil should be dried in an air current or by some other suitable method until more than 10 blows are required to close the groove. Small increments of water should then be added until the groove can be closed with 10 blows. Dry soil shall not be added to increase the number of blows required to close the groove.

(d) When the lower edges of the tow portions of the soil cake flow together for a distance of approximately ½ in. as shown in the illustration at the bottom of Fig. 2, after 10 blows have struck, the moisture content equals the liquid limit.

(e) A slice of soil approximately the width of the spatula, extending from edge to edge of the soil cake at right angles to the groove and including that portion of the groove in which the soil flowed together, shall be removed and placed in a suitable container. The container and soil shall then be weighed and the weight recorded. The soil in the container shall be oven-dried to constant weight at 110 C. (230 F.) and weighed. This weight shall be recorded and the loss in weight due to drying shall be recorded as the weight of water.

Calculation

15. The liquid limit is expressed as the moisture content in percentage of the weight of the oven-dried soil and shall be calculated as follows:

$$\text{Liquid limit} = \frac{\text{wt. of water}}{\text{wt. of oven-dried soil}} \times 100$$

CHECK OR REFEREE TESTS

Method to Be Used

16. In making check or referee tests, the mechanical method shall be used. The results of liquid limit tests are influenced by:

(a) The time required to make the test.

(b) The moisture content at which the test is begun.

(c) The addition of dry soil to the seasoned sample.

Procedure

17. (a) Therefore, in making the mechanical liquid limit test for check or referee purposes, the following time schedule shall be used:

(1) Mixing of soil with water—5 to 10 minutes, the longer period being used for the more plastic soils.

(2) Seasoning in the humidifier—30 minutes.

(3) Remixing before placing in the brass cup—Add 1 cc. of water and mix for 1 minute.

(4) Placing in the brass cup and testing—3 minutes.

(5) Adding water and remixing—3 minutes.

(b) No trial requiring more than 35 blows or less than 15 blows shall be recorded. In no case shall dried soil be added to the seasoned soil being tested.

Standard Methods of

Determining the Plastic Limit of Soils

AASHO Designation: T 90–56

Definition

1. The plastic limit of a soil is the lowest water content determined in accordance with the following procedure at which the soil remains plastic.

Apparatus

2. The apparatus shall consist of the following:

(a) *Evaporating Dish.*—A porcelain evaporating dish about 4½ inches in diameter.

(b) *Spatula.*—A spatula or pill knife having a blade about 3 inches in length and about ¾ inch in width.

(c) *Surface for Rolling.*—A ground glass plate or piece of smooth, unglazed paper on which to roll the sample.

(d) *Containers.*—Suitable containers, such as matched watch glasses, which will prevent loss of moisture during weighing.

(e) *Balance.*—A balance sensitive to 0.1 g.

Sample

3. (a) If the plastic limit only is required, take a quantity of soil weighing about 20 g from the thoroughly mixed portion of the material passing the No. 40 (420-micron) sieve, obtained in accordance with the Standard Method of Dry Preparation of Disturbed Soil Samples for Test (AASHO Designation: T 87) or the Standard Method of Wet Preparation of Disturbed Soil Samples for Test (AASHO Designation: T 146). Place the air-dried soil in an evaporating dish and thoroughly mix with distilled water until the mass becomes plastic enough to be easily shaped into a ball. Take a portion of this ball weighing about 8 g for the test sample.

(b) If both the liquid and plastic limits are required, take a test sample weighing about 8 g from the thoroughly wet and mixed portion of the soil prepared in accordance with the Standard Method of Test for Liquid Limit of Soils (AASHO Designation: T 89). Take the sample at any stage of the mixing process at which the mass becomes plastic enough to be easily shaped into a ball without sticking to the fingers excessively when squeezed. If the sample is taken before completion of the liquid limit test, set it aside and allow to season in air until the liquid limit test has been completed. If the sample is taken after completion of the liquid limit test, and is still too dry to permit rolling to a ⅛-in. thread, add more water.

Procedure

4. (a) Squeeze and form the 8-g test sample taken in accordance with Section 3(a) or (b) into an ellipsoidal-shape mass. Roll this mass between the fingers and the ground-glass plate or a piece of paper lying on a smooth horizontal surface with just sufficient pressure to roll the mass into a thread of uniform diameter throughout its length. The rate of rolling shall be between 80 and 90 strokes per min., counting a stroke as one complete motion of the hand forward and back to the starting position again.

(b) When the diameter of the thread becomes ⅛ in., break the thread into six or eight pieces. Squeeze the pieces together between the thumbs and fingers of both hands into a uniform mass roughly ellipsoidal in shape, and reroll. Continue this alternate rolling to a thread ⅛ in. in diameter, gathering together, kneading and rerolling, until the thread crumbles under the pressure required for rolling and the soil can no longer be rolled into a thread. The crumbling may occur when the thread has a diameter greater than ⅛ in. This shall be considered a satisfactory end point, provided the soil has been previously rolled into a thread ⅛ in. in diameter. The crumbling will manifest itself differently with the various types of soil. Some soils fall apart in numerous small aggregations of particles; others may form an outside tubular layer that starts splitting at both ends. The splitting progresses toward the middle, and finally, the thread falls apart in many small platy particles. Heavy clay soils require much pressure to deform the thread, particularly as they approach the plastic limit, and finally, the thread breaks into a series of barrel-shaped segments each about ¼ to ⅜ in. in length. At no time shall the operator attempt to produce failure at exactly ⅛-in. diameter by allowing the thread to reach ⅛ in., then reducing the rate of rolling or the hand pressure, or both, and continuing the rolling without further deformation until the thread falls apart. It is permissible, however, to reduce the total amount of deformation for feebly plastic soils by making the initial diameter of the ellipsoidal-shaped mass nearer to the required ⅛ in. final diameter.

(c) Gather the portions of the crumbled soil together and place in a suitable tared container. Weigh the container and soil and record the weight. Oven-dry the soil in the container to constant weight at 110 C. (230 F.) and weigh. Record this weight. Record the loss in weight as the weight of water.

Calculations

5. (a) Calculate the plastic limit, expressed as the water content in percentage of the weight of the over-dry soil, as follows:

$$\text{Plastic limit} = \frac{\text{wt. of water}}{\text{wt. of oven-dry soil}} \times 100$$

Report the plastic limit to the nearest whole number.

(b) Calculate the plasticity index of a soil as the difference between its liquid limit and its plastic limit, as follows:

$$\text{Plasticity index} = \text{liquid limit} - \text{plastic limit}$$

(c) Report the difference calculated as indicated in Paragraph (b) as the plasticity index, except under the following conditions:

(1) When the liquid limit or plastic limit cannot be determined, report the plasticity index as NP (non-plastic).

(2) When the soil is extremely sandy, the plastic limit test shall be made before the liquid limit. If the plastic limit cannot be determined, report both the liquid limit and plastic limit as NP.

(3) When the plastic limit is equal to, or greater than, the liquid limit, report the plasticity index as NP.

Standard Method of

Calculating the Plasticity Index of Soils

A.A.S.H.O. Designation: T 91–54

Definition

1. The plasticity index of a soil is the numerical difference between its liquid limit and its plastic limit.

Calculation

2. The plasticity index shall be calculated by the formula:

Plasticity index = liquid limit—plastic limit.

Report

3. The numerical difference calculated as indicated in Section 2 shall be reported as the plasticity index except under the following conditions:

(a) When the liquid limit or plastic limit cannot be determined, the plasticity index shall be reported as NP (nonplastic).

4. The liquid limit shall be determined in accordance with the Standard Method of Determining the Liquid Limit of Soils (A.A.S.H.O. Designation: T 89), and the plastic limit in accordance with the Standard Method of Determining the Plastic Limit of Soils (A.A.S.H.O. Designation: T 90).

Standard Method of Test for

Specific Gravity and Absorption of Coarse Aggregate

AASHO Designation: T 85–60

(ASTM Designation: C 127–59)

Scope

1. (*a*) This method of test is intended for use in making determinations of bulk and apparent specific gravity, and absorption (after 24 hr. in water) of coarse aggregate. The bulk specific gravity is the value generally desired for calculations in connection with portland-cement concrete.

(*b*) This method determines directly the bulk specific gravity as defined in the Standard Definitions of Terms Relating to Specific Gravity (AASHO Designation: M 132) or the bulk specific gravity on the basis of weight of saturated surface-dry aggregate, or the apparent specific gravity as defined in the Standard Definitions M 132.

Apparatus

2. The apparatus shall consist of the following:

(*a*) *Balance.*—A balance having a capacity of 5 kg. or more and sensitive to 0.5 g. or less.

(*b*) *Wire Basket.*—A wire basket of No. 6 or 8 mesh, approximately 8 in. in diameter and 8 in. in height.

(*c*) A suitable container for immersing the wire basket in water and suitable apparatus for suspending the wire basket from center of scale pan of balance.

Sample

3. Approximately 5 kg. of the aggregate shall be selected from the sample to be tested by the method of quartering, rejecting all material passing a ⅜-in. sieve. In the case of homogeneous aggregate, all material may be retained on a 1-in. sieve.

Procedure

4. (*a*) After thoroughly washing to remove dust or other coatings from the surface of the particles, the sample shall be dried to constant weight at a temperature of 100 to 110 C. (Note) and then immersed in water for a period of 24 hr. It shall then be removed from the water and rolled in a large absorbent cloth until all visible films of water are removed, although the surfaces of the particles still appear to be damp. The larger fragments may be individually wiped. Care should be taken to avoid evaporation during the operation of surface drying. The weight of the sample in the saturated surface-dry condition shall then be obtained. This and all subsequent weights shall be determined to the nearest 0.5 g.

NOTE: Where the absorption and specific gravity values may be utilized as a basis for designing concrete mixtures with aggregates normally used in a moist condition, the requirement of drying to constant weight may be eliminated.

(*b*) After weighing, the saturated surface-dry sample shall be placed immediately in the wire basket and its weight in water determined at 68 to 77 F (20 to 25 C).

(*c*) The sample shall then be dried to constant weight at a temperature of 100 to 110 C., cooled to room temperature, and weighed.

Bulk Specific Gravity

5. The bulk specific gravity as defined in the Standard Definitions of Terms

Relating to Specific Gravity (AASHO Designation: M 132) shall be calculated from the following formula:

$$\text{Bulk sp. gr.} = \frac{A}{B-C}$$

where:

A = weight in grams of oven-dry sample in air,
B = weight in grams of saturated surface-dry sample in air, and
C = weight in grams of saturated sample in water.

Bulk Specific Gravity (Saturated Surface-Dry Basis)

6. The bulk specific gravity on the basis of weight of saturated surface-dry aggregate shall be calculated from the following formula:

$$\text{Bulk sp. gr. (saturated surface-dry basis)} = \frac{B}{B-C}$$

Apparent Specific Gravity

7. The apparent specific gravity as defined in the Standard Definitions of Terms Relating to Specific Gravity (AASHO Designation: M 132) shall be calculated from the following formula:

$$\text{Apparent sp. gr.} = \frac{A}{A-C}$$

Absorption

8. The percentage of absorption shall be calculated from the following formula:

$$\text{Absorption, per cent} = \frac{B-A}{A} \times 100$$

Reproducibility of Results

9. Duplicate determinations should check to within 0.02 in the case of specific gravity and 0.05 per cent in the case of percentage of absorption.

——————— o ———————

Standard Methods of Test for

The Field Determination of Density of Soil In-Place

A.A.S.H.O. Designation: T 147–54

Method A

Disturbed Sample Method

Scope

1. This method of test is intended to determine the density of soil in the natural state or after compaction in an embankment by finding the weight and moisture content of a disturbed sample and measuring the volume occupied by the sample prior to removal.

Apparatus

2. *(a) Sampling Tools.*—An Iwan type auger, 4 inches or 6 inches in diameter, or other cutting tools suitable for boring a hole to the desired depth for materials containing no gravel. For gravelly soils, an ice pick, chisel, screwdriver, or other hand tools of similar type.

(b) Soil Tray and Pans.—A soil tray similar to that shown in figure 1. Pans or other containers of size and shape suitable for collecting, weighing, and drying soils. Small brush, trowel, spoon, or similar articles for taking sample from hole.

(c) Balances.—A balance or scale of 30-lb. capacity sensitive to 0.01 lb. and a 100-g capacity balance sensitive to 0.1 g.

(d) Measure.—A measure of known volume having a capacity not less than 0.1 cu. ft., having the height and diameter approximately equal.

(e) Drying Equipment.—A gasoline stove or other suitable device for drying samples in the field.

(f) Sand or Oil.—Approximately 20 pounds of dry sand or 2 gallons of lubricating oil. The viscosity of the oil should be such that it will flow freely at atmospheric temperature. SAE 40 is usually satisfactory. The sand should be clean, dry, and free-flowing. Sand passing a No. 20 sieve and retained on the No. 30 is most suitable.

Procedure

3. *(a)* The unit weight in lb. per cu. ft. of the dry sand shall be determined by pouring the sand into the measure through a funnel or from a container having a funnel spout. The measure shall be filled until the sand overflows and the excess shall be struck off with a straightedge. The weight of the dry sand in the measure shall be determined and the unit weight computed and recorded.

The unit weight of the oil in pounds per cubic foot may be found by filling the measure level full, weighing and calculating the unit weight.

In either case, the weight to be used shall be the average of not less than three determinations.

Note: An actual determination should be made rather than computing the weight per cubic foot from the specific gravity of the oil. The oil should be poured into the measure at approximately the same rate used in filling the test hole.

(b) All loose soil shall be removed from an area large enough to place the soil tray and a plane surface shall be cut for bedding the tray firmly.

(c) A hole shall be bored with an auger in fine-grained soils or dug with hand tools in gravelly or stony soils to the full depth of the soil layer to be

FIG. 1.—*Soil Tray.*

measured. All soil removed shall be placed in pans and any spoilage caught in the soil tray. All loose particles shall be removed from the hole with a large spoon or other suitable instrument. Extreme care shall be taken not to lose any soil.

(d) All soil taken from the hole shall be weighed and the weight recorded.

(e) A representative portion of soil shall be taken for moisture determination.

(f) A volume of dry sand or oil in excess of that required to fill the test hole shall be weighed and the weight recorded. Sand may be used in fine-grained soils, sand clays, or other mixtures in which a hole with smooth sides may be bored. Oil should be used in gravelly or stony materials in which the aggregate particles project from the sides of the hole. In porous materials, the oil should be poured rapidly.

(g) When sand is used the soil tray shall be removed and the sand deposited in the hole by the same procedure used in the determination of the unit weight until the hole is filled flush with the original ground surface. When oil is used the soil tray shall be left in place and the oil shall be poured until the oil

surface meets the gauge point shown on the cross bar in Figure 1. The following procedure may also be used for gauging the surface of the oil: After the area has been leveled as indicated in Section 3(b), three large-headed roofing nails shall be driven flush with the ground surface at approximately 120° intervals as reference points, and a three-point reference bar shall be set on these with a gauge point adjusted to the exact elevation of the surface of the material near the center of the hole. The reference bar shall be removed, the tray set over the area, and the hole bored or dug. After the removal of material from the hole has been completed, the tray shall be removed, the reference bar reset and the oil poured until the surface meets the gauge point. The remaining sand or oil shall be weighed and the weight recorded. After completion of the test as much of the sand or oil as can be removed from the hole without the inclusion of foreign matter should be reclaimed for use in future tests.

(h) The moisture content of the soil sample shall be determined and recorded.

Calculations

4. The weight per cubic foot of dry

soil in-place in the natural state or in the embankment shall be calculated as follows:

$$V = W_1$$
$$D_2$$
$$D_1 = \frac{W_s}{V}$$
$$D = \frac{D_1}{1 + \frac{w}{100}}$$

where:

V = volume of test hole,
W_1 = weight of sand or oil required to replace soil
D_2 = unit weight of sand or oil,
W_s = weight of wet soil taken from test hole,
D_1 = weight per cubic foot of wet soil,
D = weight per cubic foot of dry soil,
w = percentage of moisture in sample based on weight of dry soil.

Method B

Undisturbed Sample Method

Scope

1. This method of test is intended to determine the density of soil in the natural state or after compaction in an embankment by measuring the weight, volume, and moisture content of undisturbed samples.

Apparatus

2. The apparatus shall consist of the following:

(a) Sampling Tools.—Trowel, heavy spatula, knife, small spade suitable for removing sample or a drive tube sampler so designed to insure an undisturbed sample.

(b) Balances.—A balance or scale of 30-lb. capacity sensitive to 0.01 lb. and a 100-g. capacity balance sensitive to 0.1 g.

(c) Drying Equipment.—A gasoline stove or other suitable device for drying samples in the field.

(d) Coating Material.—Paraffin and a kettle suitable for melting paraffin and dipping samples.

(e) Volume Measuring Device.—An overflow device similar to that shown in figure 2.

(f) Graduate.—A glass graduate having a capacity of 500 cubic centimeters.

Sample

3. *(a)* A sample shall be obtained by marking an area of the size of the de-

sired sample and digging the soil from around it with a sharp tool such as a trowel, spatula, knife, or small spade. Care should be exercised in digging around the sample not to cause any disturbance of the soil structure. The sample should be 4 to 5 inches in diameter and the full depth of the layer for which the density is desired.

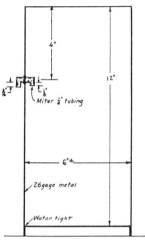

FIG. 2.—*Volumetric Displacement Apparatus.*

(b) Undisturbed samples may be obtained by driving a tube sampler into the soil layer. Care must be exercised in the use of this method to avoid disturbance of the soil structure.

Procedure

4. *(a)* Immediately upon removal of the undisturbed sample, a representative moisture sample should be taken from the wall of the hole and the moisture content (w) determined.

(b) Any loose material should be trimmed from the undisturbed sample,

the sample weighed, and the weight recorded.

(c) The trimmed sample should be immersed in melted paraffin. After the sample is coated, it shall be cooled and weighed. The gain in weight represents the weight of paraffin and the volume of the coating may be calculated by using 55 pounds per cubic foot as the weight of paraffin.

(d) The volumetric measuring apparatus (Fig. 2) shall be filled with water until the level is above the overflow. The excess water shall be permitted to drain out. The coated sample shall be immersed and the water displaced shall be weighed, or measured.

Calculations

5. The weight per cubic foot of dry soil shall be calculated as follows:

$$V_p = \frac{W_{ps} - W_s}{55}$$
$$V_s = V_{ps} - V_p$$
$$D_1 = \frac{W_s}{V_s}$$
$$D = \frac{D_1}{1 + \frac{w}{100}}$$

where:

V_p = volume of paraffin in cubic feet.
V_{ps} = volume of paraffin and soil sample in cubic feet.
V_s = volume of soil sample in cubic feet.
W_s = weight of soil sample in pounds.
W_{ps} = weight of paraffin and soil in pounds.
D_1 = unit weight of wet soil in pounds per cu. ft.
D = unit weight of dry soil in pounds per cu. ft.
w = moisture content of sample expressed as a percentage of the weight of dry soil.

Standard Method of Test for

Specific Gravity of Soils

AASHO DESIGNATION: T 100–60

(ASTM DESIGNATION: D 854–58)

Scope

1. This method of test in intended for determining the specific gravity of soils by means of a pycnometer. When the soil is composed of particles larger than the No. 4 (4760-micron) sieve, the method outlined in the Standard Method of Test for Specific Gravity and Absorption of Coarse Aggregate (AASHO Designation: T 85) shall be followed. When the soil is composed of particles both larger and smaller than the No. 4 sieve, the sample shall be separated on the No. 4 sieve and the appropriate method of test used on each portion. The specific gravity value for the soil shall be the weighted average of the two values. When the specific gravity value is to be used in calculations in connection with the hydrometer portion of the Standard Method of Mechanical Analysis of Soils (AASHO Designation: T 88) it is intended that the specific gravity test be made on that portion of the soil which passes the No. 10 (2000-micron) sieve.

Definition

2. *Specific Gravity.*[1]—Specific gravity is the ratio of the weight in air of a given volume of a material at a stated temperature to the weight in air of an equal volume of distilled water at a stated temperature.

Apparatus

3. The apparatus shall consist of the following:

(a) *Pycnometer.*—Either a volumetric flask having a capacity of at least 100

[1] This definition conforms to the Standard Definition of Terms Relating to Specific Gravity (AASHO. Designation: M 132).

ml. or a stoppered bottle having a capacity of at least 50 ml. (Note 1). The stopper shall be of the same material as the bottle, and of such size and shape that it can be easily inserted to a fixed depth in the neck of the bottle, and shall have a small hole through its center to permit the emission of air and surplus water.

NOTE 1.—The use of either the volumetric flask or the stoppered bottle is a matter of individual preference, but in general, the flask should be used when a larger sample than can be used in the stoppered bottle is needed due to maximum grain size of the sample.

(b) *Balance.*—Either a balance sensitive to 0.01 g. for use with the volumetric flask, or a balance sensitive to 0.001 g. for use with the stoppered bottle.

Calibration of Pycnometer

4. (a) The pycnometer shall be cleaned, dried, weighed, and the weight recorded. The pycnometer shall be filled with distilled water (Note 2) essentially at room temperature. The weight of the pycnometer and water, W_a, shall be determined and recorded. A thermometer shall be inserted in the water and its temperature T_i determined to the nearest whole degree.

NOTE 2.—Kerosene is a better wetting agent than water for most soils and may be used in place of distilled water for oven-dried samples.

(b) From the weight W_a determined at the observed temperature T_i a table of values of weights W_a shall be prepared for a series of temperatures that are likely to prevail when weights W_b are determined later (Note 3). These values of W_a shall be calculated as follows:

$$W_a \text{ (at } T_x) = \frac{\text{density of water at } T_x}{\text{density of water at } T_i}$$
$$\times \ (W_a \text{ (at } T_i) - W_f) + W_f$$

where:

$W_a =$ weight of pycnometer and water, in grams,

$W_f =$ weight of pycnometer, in grams,

$T_i =$ observed temperature of water, in degrees Centigrade, and

$T_x =$ any other desired temperature, in degrees Centigrade.

Note 3.—This method provides a procedure that is most convenient for laboratories making many determinations with the same pycnometer. It is equally applicable to a single determination. Bringing the pycnometer and contents to some designated temperature when weights W_a and W_b are taken, requires considerable time. It is much more convenient to prepare a table of weights W_a for various temperatures likely to prevail when weights W_b are taken. It is important that weights W_a and W_b be based on water at the same temperature. Values for the relative density of water at temperatures from 18 to 30 C. are given in Table I.

Sample

5. (a) The soil to be used in the specific gravity test may contain its natural moisture or be oven-dried. The weight of the test sample on an oven-dry basis shall be at least 25 g. when the volumetric flask is to be used, and at least 10 g. when the stoppered bottle is to be used.

(b) *Samples Containing Natural Moisture.*—When the sample contains its natural moisture, the weight of the soil, W_o on an oven-dry basis shall be determined at the end of the test by evaporating the water in an oven maintained at 110 C. (Note 4). Samples of clay soils containing their natural moisture content shall be dispersed in distilled water before placing in the flask, using the dispersing equipment specified in the Standard Method of Mechanical Analysis of Soils (AASHO Designation: T 88).

(c) *Oven-Dried Samples.*—When an oven-dried sample is to be used, the sample shall be dried for at least 12 hr., or to constant weight, in an oven maintained at 110 C. (Note 4), cooled in a desiccator, and weighed upon removal from the desiccator. The sample shall then be soaked in distilled water for at least 12 hr.

Note 4.—Drying of certain soils at 110 C. may bring about loss of moisture of composition or hydration, and in such cases drying shall be done, if desired, in reduced air pressure and at a lower temperature.

Procedure

6. (a) The sample shall be placed in the pycnometer, care being taken not to lose any of the soil in case the weight of the sample has been determined. Distilled water shall be added to fill the volumetric flask about three-fourths full or the stoppered bottle about half full.

(b) Entrapped air shall be removed by either of the following methods: (1) by subjecting the contents to a partial vacuum (air pressure not exceeding 100 mm. of mercury) or (2) by boiling gently for at least 10 min. while occasionally rolling the pycnometer to assist in the removal of the air. Subjection of the contents to reduced air pressure may be done either by connecting the pycnometer directly to an aspirator or vacuum pump, or by use of a bell jar. Some soils boil violently when subjected to reduced air pressure. It will be necessary in those cases to reduce the air pressure at a slower rate or to use a larger flask. Samples that are heated shall be cooled to room temperature.

(c) The pycnometer shall then be filled with distilled water and the outside cleaned and dried with a clean, dry cloth. The weight of the pycnometer and contents, W_b, and the temperature in degrees Centigrade, T_x, of the contents shall be determined, as described in Section 4. (Note 5)

Note 5.—The minimum volume of slurry that can be prepared by the dispersing equipment specified in Method T 88 is such that a 500 ml. flask is needed as the pycnometer.

Calculation and Report

7. (a) The specific gravity of the soil, based on water at a temperature T_x, shall be calculated as follows:

$$\text{Specific gravity, } T_x/T_x \text{ C.} = \frac{W_o}{W_o + (W_a - W_b)}$$

where:

$W_o =$ weight of sample of oven-dry soil, in grams,

$W_a =$ weight of pycnometer filled with water at temperature T_x (Note 6), in grams,

$W_b =$ weight of pycnometer filled with water and soil at temperature T_x, in grams, and

$T_x =$ temperature of the contents of the pycnometer when weight W_b was determined, in degrees Centigrade.

(b) Unless otherwise required, specific gravity values reported shall be based on water at 20 C. The value based on water at 20 C. shall be calculated from the value based on water at the observed temperature T_x, as follows:

Specific gravity, $T_x/20$ C. =

$$K \times \text{specific gravity, } T_x/T_x \text{ C.}$$

where:

$K =$ a number found by dividing the relative density of water at temperature T_x by the relative density of water at 20 C. Values for a range of temperatures are given in Table I.

(c) When it is desired to report the specific gravity value based on water at 4 C., such a specific gravity value may be calculated by multiplying the specific

TABLE I—RELATIVE DENSITY OF WATER AND CONVERSION FACTOR K FOR VARIOUS TEMPERATURES.

Temperature, deg. Cent.	Relative Density of Water	Correction Factor K
18	0.9986244	1.0004
19	0.9984347	1.0002
20	0.9982343	1.0000
21	0.9980233	0.9998
22	0.9978019	0.9996
23	0.9975702	0.9993
24	0.9973286	0.9991
25	0.9970770	0.9989
26	0.9968156	0.9986
27	0.9965451	0.9983
28	0.9962652	0.9980
29	0.9959761	0.9977
30	0.9956780	0.9974

gravity value at temperature T_x by the relative density of water at temperature T_x.

(d) When any portion of the original sample of soil is eliminated in the preparation of the test sample, the portion on which the test has been made shall be reported.

———— o ————

A.09   *Standard Method of Test for*

The Moisture-Density Relations of Soils Using A 5.5-lb. Rammer and A 12-in. Drop

AASHO Designation: T 99–57

Scope

1. *(a)* These methods of test are intended for determining the relation between the moisture content and density of soils compacted in a mold of a given size with a 5.5 lb. rammer dropped from a height of 12 in. Four alternate procedures are provided as follows:

		Sections
Method A.—A 4-in. mold: soil material passing a No. 4 (4760-micron) sieve		3 and 4
Method B.—A 6-in. mold: soil material passing a No. 4 (4760-micron) sieve		5 and 6
Method C.—A 4-in. mold: soil material passing a ¾-in. sieve		7 and 8
Method D.—A 6-in. mold: soil material passing a ¾-in. sieve		9 and 10

(b) The method to be used should be indicated in the specifications for the material being tested. If no method is specified, the provisions of Method A shall govern.

Apparatus

2. *(a) Molds.*—The molds shall be cylindrical in shape, made of metal, and shall have the capacity and dimensions indicated in Items *(1)* and *(2)* below. They shall have a detachable collar assembly approximately 2½ in. in height, to permit preparation of compacted specimens of soil-water mixtures of the desired height and volume. The molds may be of the "split" type, consisting of two half-round sections, or a section of pipe split along one element, which can be securely locked in place to form a cylinder. The mold and collar assembly shall be so constructed that it can be fastened firmly to a detachable base plate. Capacity and dimensions of the molds shall be as follows:

(1) 4.0-in. Mold having a capacity of 1/30 (0.0333) cu! ft., with an internal diameter of 4.0 ± 0.005 in. and a height of 4.584 ± 0.005 in. (see Fig. 1).

(2) 6.0-in. Mold having a capacity of 1/13.33 (0.075) cu. ft., with an internal diameter of 6.0 ± 0.005 in. and a height of 4.584 ± 0.005 in. (see Fig. 2).

(b) Rammer.—A rammer of 2-in. diameter having a flat circular face and weighing 5.5 lb. The rammer shall be equipped with a suitable arrangement to control the height of drop to a free fall of 12 in. above the elevation of the soil.

(c) Sample Extruder (optional).—A jack, lever, frame, or other device adapted for the purpose of extruding compacted specimens from the mold.

(d) Balances.—A balance or scale of at least 25-lb. capacity sensitive to 0.01 lb., and a balance of at least 1000-g capacity sensitive to 0.1 g.

(e) Drying Oven.—A thermostatically controlled drying oven capable of maintaining a temperature of 110 ± 5 C. (230 ± 9 F.) for drying moisture samples.

(f) Straightedge.—A steel straightedge 12 in. in length and having one beveled edge.

(g) Sieves.—2 in., ¾-in., and No. 4 (4760-micron) sieves conforming to the requirements of the Specifications for Sieves for Testing Purposes (AASHO Designation: M 92).

(h) Mixing Tools. — Miscellaneous tools such as mixing pan, spoon, trowel,

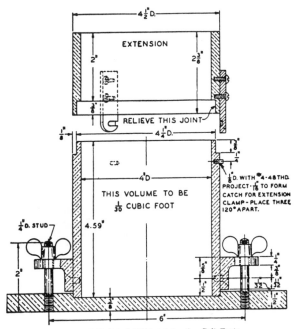

FIG. 1.—*Cylindrical Mold, 4.0 in., for Soil Tests.*

spatial, etc., or a suitable mechanical device for thoroughly mixing the sample of soil with increments of water.

METHOD A

Sample

3. (a) If the soil sample is damp when received from the field, dry it until it becomes friable under a trowel. Drying may be in air or by use of drying apparatus such that the temperature of the sample does not exceed 140 F. Then thoroughly break up the aggregations in such a manner as to avoid reducing the natural size of individual particles.

(b) Sieve an adequate quantity of the representative pulverized soil over the No. 4 (4760-micron) sieve. Discard the coarse material, if any, retained on the No. 4 sieve.

(c) Select a representative sample, weighing approximately 7 lb. or more, of the soil prepared as described in Paragraphs (a) and (b).

Procedure

4. (a) Thoroughly mix the selected representative sample with sufficient water to dampen it to approximately four percentage points below optimum moisture content.

(b) Form a specimen by compacting the prepared soil in the 4-in. mold (with collar attached) in three equal layers to give a total compacted depth of about 5 in. Compact each layer by 25 uni-

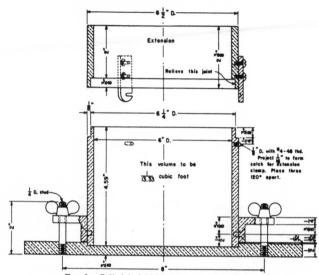

FIG. 2.—*Cylindrical Mold, 6.0-in., for Soil Tests.*

formly distributed blows from the rammer dropping free from a height of 12 in. above the elevation of the soil when a sleeve-type rammer is used, or from 12 in. above the approximate elevation of each finally compacted layer when a stationary mounted type of rammer is used. During compaction, the mold shall rest on a uniform, rigid foundation, such as provided by a cube of concrete weighing not less than 200 lb. Following compaction, remove the extension collar, carefully trim the compacted soil even with the top of the mold by means of the straightedge, and weigh. Multiply the weight of the compacted specimen and mold, minus the weight of the mold, by 30; and record the result as the wet weight per cubic foot of the compacted soil.

(c) Remove the material from the mold and slice vertically through the center. Take a representative sample of the material from one of the cut faces, weigh immediately, and dry in an oven at 110 ± 5 C. (230 ± 9 F.) for at least 12 hr., or to a constant weight to determine the moisture content. The moisture sample shall weigh not less than 100 g.

(d) Thoroughly break up the remainder of the material until it will pass a No. 4 sieve as judged by eye. Add water in sufficient amount to increase the moisture content of the soil sample by one or two percentage points, and repeat the above procedure for each increment of water added. Continue this series of determinations until there is either a decrease or no change in the wet weight per cubic foot of the compacted soil (Note).

NOTE.—This procedure has been found satisfactory in most cases. However, in instances where the soil material is fragile in character and will reduce significantly in grain size due to repeated compaction, and in cases where the soil is a heavy-textured clayey material into which it is difficult to incorporate water, a separate and new sample shall be used in each compaction test. In these cases, separate samples shall be thoroughly mixed with amounts of water sufficient to cause the moisture contents of the samples to vary by approximately two percentage points. The moisture contents selected shall bracket the optimum moisture content, thus providing samples which, when compacted, will increase in weight to the maximum density and then decrease in weight. The samples of soil-water mixtures shall be placed in covered containers and allowed to stand for not less than 12 hr. before making the moisture-density test.

METHOD B

Sample

5. Select the representative sample in accordance with Section 3 *(c)*, except that it shall weigh approximately 16 lb.

Procedure

6. Follow the same procedure as described for Method A in Section 4, except for the following: Form a specimen by compacting the prepared soil in the 6-in. mold (with collar attached) in three equal layers to give a total compacted depth of about 5 in., each layer being compacted by 56 uniformly distributed blows from the rammer. Multiply the weight of the compacted specimen and mold, minus the weight of the mold, by 13.33. Record the result as the wet weight per cubic foot of the compacted soil.

METHOD C

Sample

7. *(a)* If the soil sample is damp when received from the field, dry it until it becomes friable under a trowel. Drying may be in air or by use of drying apparatus such that the temperature of the sample does not exceed 140 F. Then thoroughly break up the aggregations in such a manner as to avoid reducing the natural size of individual particles.

(b) Sieve an adequate quantity of the representative pulverized soil over the ¾-in. sieve. Discard the coarse material, if any, retained on the ¾-in. sieve (Note).

NOTE.—If it is advisable to maintain the same percentage of coarse material (passing a 2-in. sieve and retained on a No. 4 sieve) in the moisture-density sample as in the original field sample, the material retained on the ¾-in. sieve shall be replaced as follows: Sieve an adequate quantity of the representative pulverized soil over the 2-in. and ¾-in. sieves. Discard the coarse material retained on the 2-in. sieve. Weigh the material passing the 2-in. sieve and retained on the ¾-in. sieve and replace it with an equal weight of material passing the ¾-in. sieve and retained on the No. 4 sieve. Take the material for replacement from the remaining portion of the sample.

(c) Select a representative sample, weighing approximately 12 lb., or more, of the soil prepared as described in Paragraphs *(a)* and *(b)*.

Procedure

8. *(a)* Thoroughly mix the selected representative sample with sufficient water to dampen it to approximately 4 percentage points below optimum moisture content.

(b) Form a specimen by compacting the prepared soil in the 4-in. mold (with collar attached) in three equal layers to give a total compacted depth of about 5 in. Compact each layer by 25 uniformly distributed blows from the rammer, dropping free from a height of 12 in. above the elevation of the soil when a sleeve-type rammer is used, or from 12 in. above the approximate elevation of each finally compacted layer when a stationary mounted type of rammer is used. During compaction, the mold shall rest on a uniform, rigid foundation, such as is provided by a cube of concrete weighing not less than 200 lb. Following compaction, remove the extension collar, and carefully trim the compacted soil even with the top of the mold by means of the straightedge. Holes developed in the surface by removal of coarse material shall be patched with smaller size material. Weigh the mold and moist soil. Multiply the weight of the compacted specimen and mold, minus the weight of the mold, by 30, and record the result as the wet weight per cubic foot of the compacted soil.

(c) Remove the material from the mold and slice vertically through the center. Take a representative sample of the material from one of the cut faces, weigh immediately, and dry in an oven at 110 ± 5 C. (230 ± 9 F.) for at least 12 hr., or to constant weight, to determine the moisture content. The moisture content sample shall weigh not less than 500 g.

(d) Thoroughly break up the remainder of the material until it will pass a ¾-in. sieve and 90 percent of the soil aggregations will pass a No. 4 sieve as judged by eye. Add water in sufficient amounts to increase the moisture content of the soil sample by one or two percentage points, and repeat the above procedure for each increment of water added. Continue this series of determinations until there is either a decrease or no change in the wet weight

per cubic foot of the compacted soil (see Note, Section 4 (d)).

METHOD D

Sample

9. Select the representative sample in accordance with Section 7 (c) except that it shall weigh approximately 25 lb.

Procedure

10. Follow the same procedure as described for Method C in Section 8, except for the following: Form a specimen by compacting the prepared soil in the 6-in. mold (with collar attached) in three equal layers to give a total compacted depth of about 5 in., each layer being compacted by 56 uniformly distributed blows from the rammer. Multiply the weight of the compacted specimen and mold, minus the weight of the mold, by 13.33. Record the result as the wet weight per cubic foot of the compacted soil.

CALCULATIONS AND REPORT

Calculations

11. Calculate the moisture content and the dry weight of the soil as compacted for each trial, as follows:

$$w = \frac{A - B}{B - C} \times 100$$

and

$$W = \frac{W_1}{w + 100} \times 100$$

where:

w = percentage of moisture in the specimen, based on oven dry weight of soil,
A = weight of container and wet soil,
B = weight of container and dry soil,
C = weight of container.
W = dry weight, in pounds per cubic foot of compacted soil, and
W_1 = wet weight, in pounds per cubic foot of compacted soil.

Moisture-Density Relationship

12. (a) The calculations in Section 11 shall be made to determine the moisture content and corresponding oven-dry weight (density) for each of the compacted soil samples. The oven-dry weights per cubic foot (densities) of the soil shall be plotted as ordinates and corresponding moisture contents as abscissas.

(b) *Optimum Moisture Content.*— When the densities and corresponding moisture contents for the soil have been determined and plotted as indicated in Paragraph (a), it will be found that by connecting the plotted points with a smooth line, a curve is produced. The moisture content corresponding to the peak of the curve shall be termed the "optimum moisture content" of the soil under the above compaction.

(c) *Maximum Density.*—The oven-dry weight per cubic foot of the soil at optimum moisture content shall be termed "maximum density" under the above compaction.

Standard Methods of Test for

Moisture-Density Relations of Soils Using a 10-lb Rammer and an 18-in. Drop

AASHO DESIGNATION: T 180–57

(ASTM DESIGNATION: D 1557–58 T)

Scope

1. (*a*) These methods of test are intended for determining the relationship between the moisture content and density of soils when compacted in a mold of a given size with a 10-lb rammer dropped from a height of 18 in. Four alternate procedures are provided as follows:

	Sections
Method A.—A 4-in. mold: soil material passing a No. 4 (4760-micron) sieve	3 and 4
Method B.—A 6-in. mold: soil material passing a No. 4 (4760-micron) sieve	5 and 6
Method C.—A 4-in. mold: soil material passing a ¾-in sieve	7 and 8
Method D.—A 6-in. mold: soil material passing a ¾-in. sieve	9 and 10

(*b*) The method to be used should be indicated in the specifications for the material being tested. If no method is specified, the provisions of Method A shall govern.

Apparatus

2. (*a*) *Molds.*—The molds shall be cylindrical in shape, made of metal, and shall have the capacity and dimensions indicated in Items (*1*) and (*2*) below. They shall have a detachable collar assembly approximately 2½ in. in height, to permit preparation of compacted specimens of soil-water mixtures of the desired height and volume. The molds may be of the "split" type, consisting of two half-round sections or a section of pipe split along one element, which can be securely locked in place to form a cylinder. The mold and collar assembly shall be so constructed that it can be fastened firmly to a detachable base plate. Capacity and dimensions of the molds shall be as follows:

(*1*) *4.0-in. Mold* having a capacity of $\frac{1}{30}$ (0.0333) cu ft, with an internal diameter of 4.0 ± 0.005 in. and a height of 4.584 ± 0.005 in. (Fig. 1).

(*2*) *6.0-in. Mold* having a capacity of $\frac{1}{13.33}$ (0.075) cu ft, with an internal diameter of 6.0 ± 0.005 in. and a height of 4.584 ± 0.005 in. (Fig. 2).

(*b*) *Rammer.*—A metal rammer having a 2-in. diameter circular face and weighing 10.0 lb. The rammer shall be equipped with a suitable arrangement to control the height of drop to a free fall of 18 in. above the elevation of the soil.

(*c*) *Sample Extruder (optional).*—A jack, lever frame, or other device adapted for the purpose of extruding compacted specimens from the mold.

(*d*) *Balances.*—A balance or scale of at least 25-lb capacity sensitive to 0.01 lb, and a balance of at least 1000-g capacity sensitive to 0.1 g.

(*e*) *Drying Oven.*—A thermostatically controlled drying oven capable of maintaining a temperature of 230 ± 9 F (110 ± 5 C) for drying moisture samples.

(*f*) *Straightedge.*—A steel straightedge 12 in. in length and having one beveled edge.

(*g*) *Sieves.*—2-in., ¾-in., and No. 4 (4760-micron) sieves conforming to the requirements of the Specifications for Sieves for Testing Purposes (AASHO Designation: M92).

(*h*) *Mixing Tools.*—Miscellaneous tools such as mixing pan, spoon, trowel spatula, etc., or a suitable mechanical device for thoroughly mixing the sample of soil with increments of water.

Method A

Sample

3. (a) If the soil sample is damp when received from the field, dry it until it becomes friable under a trowel. Dry-

(b) Sieve an adequate quantity of the representative pulverized soil over the No. 4 (4760-micron) sieve. Discard the coarse material, if any, retained on the No. 4 sieve.

(c) Select a representative sample, weighing approximately 7 lb or more, of the soil prepared as described in Paragraphs (a) and (b).

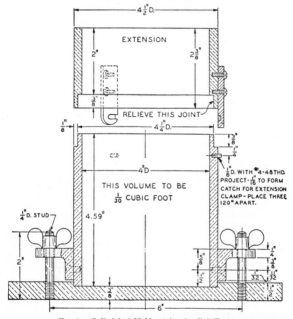

Fig. 1.—*Cylindrical Mold, 4.0-in., for Soil Tests.*

ing may be in air or by use of drying apparatus such that the temperature of the sample does not exceed 140 F (60 C). Then thoroughly break up the aggregations in such a manner as to avoid reducing the natural size of individual particles.

Procedure

4. (a) Thoroughly mix the selected representative sample with sufficient water to dampen it to approximately four percentage points below optimum moisture content.

(b) Form a specimen by compacting

the prepared soil in the 4-in. mold (with collar attached) in five equal layers to give a total compacted depth of about 5 in. Compact each layer by 25 uniformly distributed blows from the rammer dropping free from a height of 18 in. above the elevation of the soil when a sleeve-type rammer is used, or from 18 in. above the approximate elevation of each finally compacted layer when a stationary mounted type of rammer is used. During compaction, the mold shall rest

(c) Remove the material from the mold and slice vertically through the center. Take a representative sample of the material from one of the cut faces, weigh immediately, and dry in an oven at 230 ± 9 F (110 ± 5 C) for at least 12 hr, or to a constant weight to determine the moisture content. The moisture sample shall weigh not less than 100 g.

(d) Thoroughly break up the remainder of the material until it will pass a

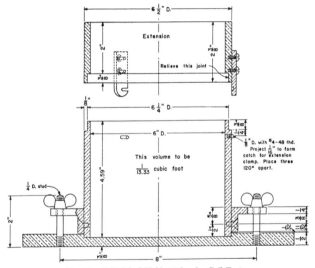

Fig. 2.—*Cylindrical Mold, 6.0-in., for Soil Tests.*

on a uniform, rigid foundation, such as provided by a cube of concrete weighing not less than 200 lb. Following compaction, remove the extension collar, carefully trim the compacted soil even with the top of the mold by means of the straightedge, and weigh. Multiply the weight of the compacted specimen and mold, minus the weight of the mold, by 30. Record the result as the wet weight per cubic foot of the compacted soil.

No. 4 sieve as judged by eye. Add water in sufficient amounts to increase the moisture content of the soil sample by one or two percentage points, and repeat the above procedure for each increment of water added. Continue this series of determinations until there is either a decrease or no change in the wet weight per cubic foot of the compacted soil (Note 1).

NOTE 1.—This procedure has been found satisfactory in most cases. However, in instances where the soil material is fragile in character and will reduce significantly in grain size due to repeated compaction, and in cases where the soil is a heavy-textured clayey material into which it is difficult to incorporate water, a separate and new sample shall be used in each compaction test. In these cases, separate samples shall be thoroughly mixed with amounts of water sufficient to cause the moisture contents of the samples to vary by approximately two percentage points. The moisture contents selected shall bracket the optimum moisture content, thus providing samples which, when compacted, will increase in weight to the maximum density and then decrease in weight. The samples of soil-water mixtures shall be placed in covered containers and allowed to stand for not less than 12 hr before making the moisture-density test.

METHOD B

Sample

5. Select the representative sample in accordance with Section 3 (c), except that it shall weigh approximately 16 lb.

Procedure

6. Follow the same procedure as described for Method A in Section 4, except for the following: Form a specimen by compacting the prepared soil in the 6-in. mold (with collar attached) in five equal layers to give a total compacted depth of about 5 in., each layer being compacted by 56 uniformly distributed blows from the rammer. Multiply the weight of the compacted specimen and mold, minus the weight of the mold, by 13.33. Record the result as the wet weight per cubic foot of the compacted soil.

METHOD C

Sample

7. (a) If the soil sample is damp when received from the field, dry it until it becomes friable under a trowel. Drying may be in air or by use of drying apparatus such that the temperature of the samples does not exceed 140 F (60 C). Then thoroughly break up the aggregations in such a manner as to avoid reducing the natural size of individual particles.

(b) Sieve an adequate quantity of the representative pulverized soil over the ¾-in. sieve. Discard the coarse material, if any, retained on the ¾-in. sieve (Note 2).

NOTE 2.—If it is advisable to maintain the same percentage of coarse material (passing a 2-in. sieve and retained on a No. 4 (4760-micron) sieve in the moisture-density sample as in the original field sample, the material retained on the ¾-in.

sieve shall be replaced as follows: Sieve an adequate quantity of the representative pulverized soil over the 2-in. and ¾-in. sieves. Discard the coarse material retained on the 2-in. sieve. Remove the material passing the 2-in. sieve and retained on the ¾-in. sieve and replace it with an equal weight of material passing the ¾-in. sieve and retained on the No. 4 sieve. Take the material for replacement from the remaining portion of the sample.

(c) Select a representative sample, weighing approximately 12 lb or more, of the soil prepared as described in Paragraphs (a) and (b).

Procedure

8. (a) Thoroughly mix the selected representative sample with sufficient water to dampen it to approximately four percentage points below optimum moisture content.

(b) Form a specimen by compacting the prepared soil in the 4-in. mold (with collar attached) in five equal layers to give a total compacted depth of about 5 in. Compact each layer by 25 uniformly distributed blows from the rammer, dropping free from a height of 18 in. above the elevation of the soil when a sleeve-type rammer is used, or from 18 in. above the approximate elevation of each finally compacted layer when a stationary mounted type of rammer is used. During compaction, the mold shall rest on a uniform, rigid foundation, such as is provided by a cube of concrete weighing not less than 200 lb. Following compaction, remove the extension collar and carefully trim the compacted soil even with the top of the mold by means of the straight-edge. Holes developed in the surface by removal of coarse material shall be patched with smaller size material. Weigh the mold and moist soil. Multiply the weight of the compacted specimen and mold, minus the weight of the mold, by 30, and record the result as the wet weight per cubic foot of the compacted soil.

(c) Remove the material from the mold and slice vertically through the center. Take a representative sample of the material from one of the cut faces, weigh immediately, and dry in an oven at 230 ± 9 F (110 ± 5 C) for at least 12 hr, or to constant weight, to determine the moisture content. The moisture content sample, shall weigh not less than 500 g.

(d) Thoroughly break up the remainder of the material until it will pass a ¾-in. sieve and 90 per cent of the soil aggregations will pass a No. 4 sieve as judged by eye. Add water in sufficient amounts to increase the moisture content of the soil sample by one or two percentage points, and repeat the above procedure for each increment of water added. Continue this series of determinations until there is either a decrease or no change in the wet weight per cubic foot of the compacted soil (Note 1).

METHOD D

Sample

9. Select the representative sample in accordance with Section 7 (c), except that it shall weigh approximately 25 lb.

Procedure

10. Follow the same procedure as described for Method C in Section 7, except for the following: Form a specimen by compacting the prepared soil in the 6-in. mold (with collar attached) in five equal layers to give a total compacted depth of about 5 in., each layer being compacted by 56 uniformly distributed blows from the rammer. Multiply the weight of the compacted specimen and mold, minus the weight of the mold, by 13.33. Record the result as the wet weight per cubic foot of the compacted soil.

CALCULATIONS AND REPORT

Calculations

11. Calculate the moisture content and the dry weight of the soil as compacted for each trial, as follows:

$$w = \frac{A - B}{B - C} \times 100$$

and

$$W = \frac{W_1}{w + 100} \times 100$$

where:

w = percentage of moisture in the specimen,
A = weight of container and wet soil,
B = weight of container and dry soil,
C = weight of container,
W = dry weight, in pounds per cubic foot of compacted soil, and
W_1 = wet weight, in pounds per cubic foot of compacted soil.

Moisture-Density Relationship

12. (a) The calculations in Section 11 shall be made to determine the moisture content and corresponding oven-dry weight (density) for each of the compacted soil samples. The oven-dry weights per cubic foot (densities) of the soil shall be plotted as ordinates and corresponding moisture contents as abscissas.

(b) Optimum Moisture Content.— When the densities and corresponding moisture contents for the soil have been determined and plotted as indicated in Paragraph (a), it will be found that by connecting the plotted points with a smooth line, a curve is produced. The moisture content corresponding to the peak of the curve shall be termed the "optimum moisture content" of the soil under the above compaction.

(c) Maximum Density.—The oven-dry weight per cubic foot of the soil at "optimum moisture content" shall be termed "maximum density" under the above compaction.

Report

13. The report shall include the following:

(1) The method used (Method A, B, C, or D),

(2) The optimum moisture content,

(3) The maximum density, and

(4) In Methods C and D, whether the ¾-in. material was removed or replaced.

———— o ————

State of California

Department of Public Works

Division of Highways

Method No. Calif. 903-B

MATERIALS AND RESEARCH DEPARTMENT

Scope

This method describes the procedure for the direct calibration of expansion pressure devices, employed in the R-value test (Test Method No. Calif. 301), by the use of a counter type weighing scale, modified with a hold-down table and platform stud arrangement to accommodate the expansion pressure device.

Procedure

A. Apparatus (See Figures I, II and III)

1. One counter type scale, minimum capacity 100 lbs. accurate to one oz., arranged with the attachment of items 2 and 3 below as shown in Figure I.

2. Hold-down table and clamps.

3. Platform stud and pressure thimble.

B. Calibration Procedure

The brass shims under the spring steel bars on the Expansion Pressure (E. P.) devices must be adjusted properly in order to maintain the correct relationship between the deflection of the bar and the force generated by the test specimen. The calibration procedure is as follows:

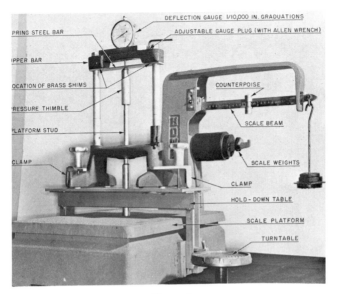

Figure I

1. Remove the turntable from the E. P. device.

2. Set the E. P. device on the hold-down table so that the platform stud passes through the threaded turntable hole. The feet of the E. P. device should rest firmly upon the three seating buttons fixed on the top of the hold-down table and the platform stud *must not* touch the side of the threaded turntable hole. The pressure thimble on the end of the platform stud should be centered as nearly as possible on the spring steel bar (both longitudinally and transversely on the bar). Due to differences in the manufacture of some E. P. devices, precise centering is not always possible. However the calibration is *not* sensitive to the slight eccentricity normally resulting from this cause. Lock the E. P. device feet in place with the clamps provided on the hold-down table.

3. With the pressure thimble *not* touching the spring steel bar (as shown in Fig. I), place the deflection gauge in position on top of the E. P. device and zero the dial by means of the adjustable gauge plug.

— 233 —

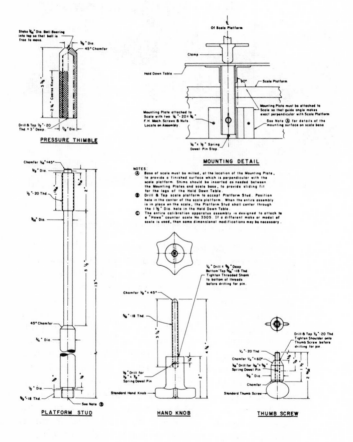

Figure II

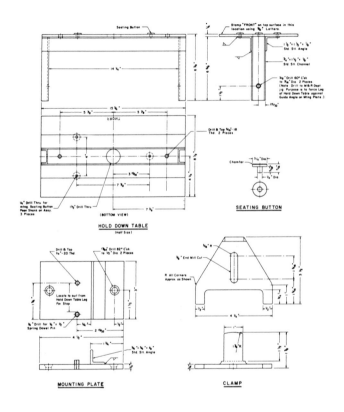

Figure III

4. Balance the beam on the scale by moving the counterpoise to the appropriate position. This balances out the weight of the stud and pressure thimble.

> **NOTE: Make sure that the pressure thimble is *not* engaged with the spring steel bar on the E. P. device in this operation.**

5. Add weights to the scale beam in 10-lb. increments up to a total weight of 40 lbs. (leaving counterpoise set at weight found above for stud and pressure thimble). At each increment balance the scale beam by adjusting the pressure thimble in an upward direction so that it applies the necessary balancing load against the spring steel bar in the E. P. device, and record the reading of the deflection gauge. When the E. P. device is in proper adjustment, the readings obtained at each load should correspond to those listed in Table I within ± 0.0001 in.

TABLE I

Load Deflection Values Required for the Correct Adjustment of Expansion Pressure Devices

Applied load (lb.)	Dial Reading (in.)*
10	.0021
20	.0042
30	.0063
40	.0084

*The dial readings are determined from the formula $D = 0.00021 \ P$ Where:

D = Deflection gauge dial reading in 0.0001 in.

P = Load in lbs. applied to the spring steel bar in the E. P. device.

6. When the dial readings do not correspond to those in Table I above within the tolerance of ± 0.0001

in., it will be necessary to alter the deflection characteristics of the spring steel bar in the E. P. device by repositioning the brass shims. This is accomplished by loosening the upper bar on the E. P. device and adjusting the position of the shims on the longitudinal axis of the spring steel bar until the dial checks within ± 0.0001 in. of the values given in Table I at each load.

> **NOTE: The E. P. device may remain clamped on the hold-down table when loosening the nuts at the top of the device and adjusting the shims. However, the pressure thimble should be backed off until it does *not* engage the spring steel bar before starting this operation.**

7. All Expansion Pressure devices should be recalibrated at least once every 2 months. In cases where extreme expansion pressure has left a permanent set in the spring steel bar, the E. P. device must be recalibrated before using again. It is generally considered that "extreme pressure" has occurred when a dial reading, at the end of a 16-24 hr. test period, exceeds 0.01 inch (one turn around the dial).

REFERENCE

Test Method No. Calif. 301

A.12 METHOD OF FABRICATING PAPER BASKETS FOR STABILOMETER SPECIMENS

State of California

Department of Public Works

Division of Highways

Method No. Calif. 904-B

MATERIALS AND RESEARCH DEPARTMENT

Scope

This method covers the procedure for fabricating paper baskets that are used in Test Methods No. Calif. 301 and 304.

Procedure

A. Apparatus

Basket-making device consisting of a 3⅞-inch diameter cylindrical wooden block and a ½-inch masking tape dispenser. See Figure I.

> **Note: The basket-making device specified in Method No. Calif. 904-A is still satisfactory for this revised method. However, the stapler is no longer needed and should be removed and put to other uses.**

B. Materials

1. Strips of notched paper: 60-lb. brown Kraft paper 2½ inches x 13⅜ inches with slots 1⅞ inches in length and ¾ inch apart down the center of the strip. See Figure II. Service & Supply Stock No. 69530.

2. 4-inch diameter cardboard disks (for Calif. 304).

3. 4-inch diameter phosphor-bronze perforated exudation pressure disks (for Calif. 301).

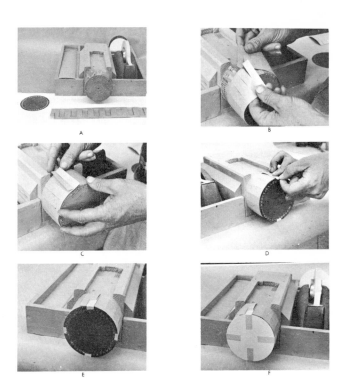

Figure I.

4. ½-inch width masking tape.

C. Fabrication Procedure

The procedure for R-value specimens (Calif. 301) and stabilometer specimens (Calif. 304) is identical. The materials used differ in that phosphor-bronze perforated disks are used for R-value specimens and cardboard disks are used for stabilometer specimens.

Use the following procedure for fabricating baskets:

Step 1. Take a piece of slotted paper and fold around the cylindrical wooden block hooking the slotted ends together. See Photos B and C of Figure I.

Step 2. Using 4 strips of ½-inch masking tape, tape

SPECIFICATIONS FOR THE SLOTTED PAPER USED IN FABRICATING
PAPER BASKETS·FOR STABILOMETER
SPECIMENS

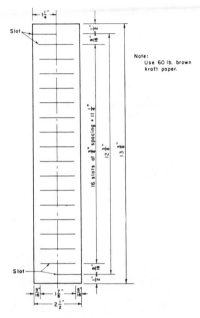

Figure II.

phosphor-bronze disk to the paper so that the holes in the disk are not obscured in the process. See Photos D and E of Figure I.

For bituminous specimen baskets, merely substitute a cardboard disk in lieu of the phosphor-bronze disk, as shown in Photo F of Figure I.

Note: Do not under any circumstances use an additional amount of tape to secure bottoms.

REFERENCES

Test Method No. Calif. 301

Test Method No. Calif. 304

Standard Method for

Plastic Fines in Graded Aggregates and Soils by Use of the Sand Equivalent Test

AASHO Designation: T 176–56

Scope

1. This test is intended to serve as a rapid field test to show the relative amounts of plastic fines in graded aggregates and soils.

Apparatus

2. *(a)* A transparent graduated measuring cylinder having an internal diameter of 1¼ inches, a height of about 17 inches, and graduations up to 15 inches by tenths, beginning at the bottom.

(b) An irrigator tube made of ¼-inch outside diameter brass or copper tubing. One end is closed to form a wedge-shaped point. Two holes (drill size 60) are drilled laterally through the flat side of the wedge near the point.

(c) A one-gallon bottle with siphon assembly consisting of a two-hole stopper and a bent copper tube. The bottle is placed three feet above the working table.

(d) A length of ³⁄₁₆-inch rubber tubing with a pinch clamp for shutting off the flow. This tubing is used to connect the irrigator tube to the siphon assembly.

(e) A weighted foot consisting of a metal rod 18 inches long having at the lower end a 1-inch diameter conical foot. The foot has three small centering screws to center it loosely in the cylinder. A cap to fit the top of the cylinder fits loosely around the rod and serves to center the top of the rod in the cylinder. A weight is attached to the top end of the rod to give an assembly weight of 1 kilogram.

(f) A 3-ounce size measuring can (88 ml capacity).

(g) A wide-mouth funnel for transferring soil into the cylinder.

(h) Stock solution.

454 grams (1 lb.) tech. anhydrous calcium chloride

2050 grams (1640 ml) U.S.P. glycerine

47 grams (45 ml) formaldehyde (40 per cent by volume)

Dissolve the calcium chloride in ½-gallon of water. Cool and filter through Whatman No. 12 or equal filter paper. Add the glycerine and formaldehyde to the filtered solution, mix well and dilute to one gallon. The water may be distilled or good quality tap water.

(i) *Working solution.*—Dilute 88 ml of the stock solution to 1 gallon with tap water. The graduated cylinder filled to 4.4 inches contains the required 88 ml. Questionable water may be tested by comparing results of sand equivalent tests on identical samples using solutions made with the questionable water and with distilled water.

Procedure

3. *(a) Preparation of Sample.*—The material used in the test is the portion of the sample passing the No. 4 sieve. Therefore, if the sample contains coarse rock it must be screened on a No. 4 sieve and the lumps of finer material must be broken down. If the original sample is not damp it should be dampened with water before screening. If the coarse aggregate carries a coating that is not removed by the screening operation, dry the coarse aggregate and rub it between the hands, adding the resulting dust to the fines.

(b) Start the siphon by blowing into

FIG. 2.—*Agitation of Sample.*

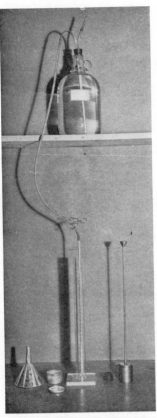

FIG. 1.—*Sand Equivalent Apparatus.*

the top of the solution bottle through a short piece of tubing while the pinch clamp is open. The apparatus is now ready for use.

(c) Siphon the working solution into the cylinder to a depth of 4 inches.

(d) Pour 1 measuring can full of the

prepared soil sample into the cylinder. One can-full amounts to about 110 grams of average loose material. Tap the bottom of the cylinder firmly on the heel of the hand several times to dislodge any air bubbles and to aid in wetting the sample. Allow to stand for 10 minutes.

(e) At the end of the 10-minute period stopper the cylinder and shake vigorously from side to side, holding in a *horizontal* position as illustrated in Fig. 2. Make 90 cycles in about 30 seconds, using a "throw" of about 8 inches. A cycle consists of a complete back and forth motion. To successfully shake the sample at this speed, it will be necessary for the operator to shake with the forearms only, relaxing the body and shoulders.

(f) Remove the stopper and insert the irrigator tube. Rinse down the sides, then insert the tube to the bottom of the cylinder. Wash the clayey material upward out of the sand by applying a gentle stabbing action with the tube while revolving the cylinder slowly. When the liquid level rises to 15 inches raise the irrigator tube slowly without shutting off the flow so that the liquid level is maintained at about 15 inches

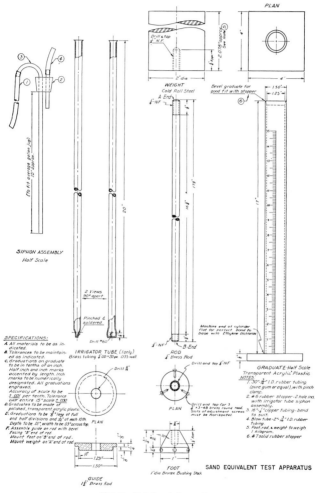

Fig. 3.—*Details of Apparatus.*

while the tube is being withdrawn. Regulate the flow just before the tube is entirely withdrawn and adjust the final level to 15 inches. Allow to stand undisturbed for exactly 20 minutes. Any vibration or movement of the cylinder during this time will interfere with the normal settling rate of the suspended clay and will cause an erroneous result.

(g) At the end of the 20-minute period record the level of the top of the clay suspension. Read to the nearest 0.1 inch.

(h) Gently lower the weighted foot into the cylinder until it comes to rest on the sand. Twist the rod slightly without pushing down until one of the centering screws can be seen. Record the level at the center of the screw and take this as the reading at the top of the sand.

(i) Calculate the sand equivalent by using the following formula:

$$SE = \frac{\text{Reading at top of sand}}{\text{Reading at top of clay}} \times 100$$

If the sand equivalent value is less than the specified value, perform two additional tests on the same material and take the average of the three as the sand equivalent.

(j) To empty the cylinder, stopper and shake up and down in an inverted position until the sand plug is disintegrated, then empty immediately. Rinse twice with water. Do not expose plastic cylinder to direct sunlight any more than is necessary.

———— o ————

APPENDIX B

GLOSSARY

B.01 Capillary Action (Capillarity)—the rise or movement of water in the interstices of a soil due to capillary forces.

B.02 Capillary Water—water subject to the influence of capillary action.

B.03 Cohesion—all of the shear strength of a soil not due to friction. It is the portion of the shear strength of a soil indicated by the "C" in Coulomb's equation, $s = c + p \tan \phi$.

B.04 Compaction—densification due almost entirely to the expulsion of air from the soil mass by mechanical manipulation.

B.05 Compressibility—that portion of the decrease in volume of a soil mass resulting from the expulsion of only the pore water when subjected to load.

B.06 Consolidation— (see compressibility)

B.07 Deflection—the amount of downward vertical movement of a surface due to the application of a load to the surface.

B.08 Elasticity—ability of a soil to return to its original shape after having been deformed by a load for a short period of time.

B.09 Frost Susceptibility— soil susceptible to freezing because of a water table close enough to the frost line to feed growing ice lenses and characteristics favorable to the rapid movement of capillary water upward from the water table.

B.10 Liquid Limit—the water content, as determined by the standard liquid limit test, at which a soil passes from a plastic to a liquid state.

B.11 Maximum Density (Maximum Unit Weight)—the dry unit weight defined by the peak of a compaction curve.

B.12 Moisture Content— see Water Content.

B.13 Optimum Moisture Content—the water content at which a soil can be compacted to the maximum dry unit weight by a given compactive effort.

B.14 Pedology—the science that treats of soils, including their nature, properties, formation, functioning, behavior and response to use and management.

B.15 Permeability—ease or difficulty with which water will flow or pass through the pores of a soil.

B.16 Plastic Limit—the lowest water content, as determined by the standard plastic limit test, at which a soil remains plastic.

B.17 Plasticity—ability of a soil to be deformed rapidly without cracking or crumbling and then maintain that deformed shape after the deforming force has been released.

B.18 Plasticity Index—the difference between the liquid limit and the plastic limit.

B.19 Porosity—the ratio, usually expressed as a percentage, of (1) the volume of voids of a given soil mass to (2) the total volume of the soil mass.

B.20 Rebound Deflection—the amount of vertical rebound of a surface that occurs when a load is removed from the surface.

B.21 Residual Deflection—difference between original and final elevations of a surface resulting from the application and removal of one or more loads to and from the surface.

B.22 Shearing Strength—the maximum resistance of a soil to shearing stresses. It is the result of friction between the particles, and cohesion.

B.23 Shrinkage and Swell—volume change due to build-up and release of capillary tensile stresses within the soil's pore water.

B.24 Soil—Any earthern material, excluding bed rock, composed of loosely bound mineral grains of various sizes and shapes, organic material, water and gases.

B.25 Soil Horizon—one of the layers of the soil profile, distinguished principally by its texture, color, structure, and chemical content.

"A" Horizon—the uppermost layer of a soil profile from which inorganic colloids and other soluble materials have been leached. Usually contains remnants of organic life.

"B" Horizon—the layer of a soil profile in which material leached from the overlying "A" horizon is accumulated.

"C" Horizon—undisturbed parent material from which the overlying soil profile has been developed.

"D" Layer—any layer underlying the "C" horizon, or the "B" if no "C" is present, which is unlike the horizon above it.

B.26 Soil Profile—vertical sections of a soil, showing the nature and sequence of the various layers, as developed by deposition or weathering, or both.

B.27 Soil Structure—the arrangement and state of aggregation of soil particles in a soil mass.

B-28 Soil Texture (Grain Size Distribution, Graduation)—proportion of a material of each grain size present in a given soil.

B.29 Void Ratio—the ratio of (1) the volume of void space to (2) the volume of solid particles in a given soil mass.

B.30 Water Content (Moisture Content)—the ratio, expressed as a percentage, of (1) the weight of water in a given soil mass to (2) the weight of solid particles.

INDEX

105166

THE ASPHALT INSTITUTE

EXECUTIVE OFFICES AND LABORATORIES

Asphalt Institute Building

College Park, Maryland 20740

MEMBERS OF THE ASPHALT INSTITUTE

(As of November 1, 1966)

The Asphalt Institute is an international, nonprofit association sponsored by members of the petroleum asphalt industry to serve both users and producers of asphaltic materials through programs of engineering service, research and education. Membership is limited to refiners of asphalt from crude petroleum. Institute members provide quality products and advocate quality construction and timely maintenance.

ALLIED MATERIALS CORPORATION
Oklahoma City

AMERICAN OIL COMPANY
Chicago

APCO OIL CORPORATION
Oklahoma City

ASHLAND OIL & REFINING COMPANY
Ashland, Kentucky

ATLANTIC RICHFIELD COMPANY
Atlantic Division—Philadelphia
Richfield Division—Los Angeles

BRITISH AMERICAN OIL COMPANY LTD.
Toronto, Ontario, Canada

BP CANADA LIMITED
Montreal, Quebec, Canada

BRITISH PETROLEUM COMPANY LTD.
London, England

BYERLYTE COMPANY OF KOPPERS COMPANY, INC.
Cleveland

CANADIAN PETROFINA LIMITED
Montreal, Quebec, Canada

CHAMPLIN PETROLEUM COMPANY
Fort Worth, Texas

CHEVRON ASPHALT COMPANY
San Francisco and Baltimore

CITIES SERVICE OIL COMPANY
Tulsa

COMPANIA ESPANOLA DE PETROLEOS, S.A.
  Madrid, Spain
CONTINENTAL OIL COMPANY
  Houston
DOUGLAS OIL COMPANY OF CALIFORNIA
  Los Angeles
EDGINGTON OIL REFINERIES, INC.
  Long Beach, California
ESSO STANDARD EASTERN, INC.
  New York
FARMERS UNION CENTRAL EXCHANGE, INC.
  Laurel, Montana
GOLDEN BEAR OIL COMPANY
  A Division of Witco Chemical Company, Inc.
  Los Angeles
GREAT NORTHERN OIL COMPANY
  St. Paul
Industrial Asphalt, Inc., Agent for
GULF OIL CORPORATION
  Los Angeles
HUMBLE OIL & REFINING COMPANY
  Houston and New York
HUNT OIL COMPANY
  Dallas
HUSKY OIL CANADA LTD.
  Calgary, Alberta, Canada
HUSKY OIL COMPANY
  Cody, Wyoming
IMPERIAL OIL LIMITED
  Toronto, Ontario, Canada
KERR-McGEE CORPORATION
  Oklahoma City
LEONARD REFINERIES, INC.
  Alma, Michigan
LION OIL COMPANY
  Hydrocarbons Division, Monsanto Company
  El Dorado, Arkansas
MACMILLAN RING-FREE OIL CO., INC.
  New York and El Dorado, Ark.
MARATHON OIL COMPANY
  Findlay, Ohio
MOBIL OIL CORPORATION
  New York
MOBIL OIL CORPORATION
  International Division—New York

MURPHY OIL CORPORATION
El Dorado, Arkansas

NESTE OY
Helsinki, Finland

NEWHALL REFINING CO., INC.
Newhall, California

NORTHWESTERN REFINING COMPANY
St. Paul Park, Minnesota

AB NYNAS-PETROLEUM
Nynashamn, Sweden

PAZ OIL COMPANY LIMITED
Haifa, Israel

PHILLIPS PETROLEUM COMPANY
Bartlesville, Oklahoma

RAFFINERIE BELGE DE PETROLES, S.A.
Antwerp, Belgium

SHELL CANADA LIMITED
Toronto, Ontario, Canada

SHELL INTERNATIONAL PETROLEUM CO., LTD.
London, England

SHELL OIL COMPANY
New York and San Francisco

SINCLAIR REFINING COMPANY
New York

SOUTHLAND OIL COMPANY
Yazoo City, Mississippi

STANDARD OIL COMPANY
OF BRITISH COLUMBIA, LTD.
Vancouver, B.C., Canada

THE STANDARD OIL COMPANY
(An Ohio Corporation)
Cleveland

SUN OIL COMPANY
Philadelphia

SUNRAY DX OIL COMPANY
Tulsa

UNION OIL COMPANY OF CALIFORNIA
Los Angeles

U. S. OIL AND REFINING COMPANY
Los Angeles

WITCO CHEMICAL COMPANY, INC.
Pioneer Products Division
New York

CONTRIBUTOR

ENVOY PETROLEUM CO.
Long Beach, California

INSTITUTE ENGINEERING OFFICES

(As of November 1, 1966)

EASTERN DIVISION

WASHINGTON, D.C. 20006—1901 Pennsylvania Ave., N.W.
  Connecticut, Delaware, District of Columbia, Kentucky, Maine, Maryland, Massachusetts, New Hampshire, New Jersey, New York, Ohio, Pennsylvania, Rhode Island, Vermont, Virginia, West Virginia

BOSTON, MASS.—(Address: 599 North Ave., Wakefield 01880)
  Connecticut, Maine, Massachusetts, New Hampshire, Rhode Island, Vermont

ALBANY, N. Y. 12206—50 Colvin Ave.
  New York State (except New York City, Westchester County and Long Island)

NEW YORK, N. Y. 10020—1270 Ave. of the Americas
  New York City, Westchester County, Long Island, New Jersey

HARRISBURG, PA. 17102—800 N. Second St.
  Pennsylvania

RICHMOND, VA. 23219—Travelers Bldg.
  Virginia

COLUMBUS, OHIO 43215—50 W. Broad St.
  Ohio

LOUISVILLE, KY. 40207—4050 Westport Road
  Kentucky, West Virginia

SOUTHERN DIVISION

NEW ORLEANS, LA. 70130—John Hancock Bldg.
  Alabama, Arkansas, Florida, Georgia, Louisiana, Mississippi, New Mexico, North Carolina, Oklahoma, South Carolina, Tennessee, Texas

AUSTIN, TEXAS 78701—Perry-Brooks Bldg.
  Texas

OKLAHOMA CITY, OKLA. 73102—Kermac Bldg.
  Arkansas, Oklahoma, Northern Texas

SANTA FE, N. MEX. 87501—10 Radio Plaza
  New Mexico, Western Texas

MONTGOMERY, ALA. 36104—79 Commerce St.
  Alabama, Tennessee

ATLANTA, GA. 30326—3384 Peachtree Road
  Georgia

TALLAHASSEE, FLA. 32303—Tallahassee Bldg.
  Florida

RALEIGH, N. C. 27605—2016 Cameron St.
  North Carolina, South Carolina

NORTHERN DIVISION

ST. PAUL, MINN. 55104—276 N. Snelling Ave.
Colorado, Idaho, Illinois, Indiana, Iowa,
Kansas, Michigan, Minnesota, Missouri,
Montana, Nebraska, North Dakota, South
Dakota, Utah, Wisconsin, Wyoming

EAST LANSING, MICH. 48823—1019 Trowbridge Road
Indiana, Michigan

INDIANAPOLIS, IND. 46205—4165 Millersville Road
Indiana

SPRINGFIELD, ILL. 62703—2606 S. Sixth St.
Illinois (except Chicago), St. Louis County,
Missouri

CHICAGO. ILL. 60639—6261 W. Grand Ave.
Wisconsin, Metropolitan Chicago

MADISON, WISC. 53711—4333 Nakoma Rd.
Wisconsin

KANSAS CITY, MO. 64112—612 W. 47th St.
Kansas, Missouri (except St. Louis Co.),
Nebraska, North Dakota, South Dakota

JEFFERSON CITY, MO. 65101—616 Howard St.
Missouri (except St. Louis Co.)

OMAHA, NEBR. 68132—6901 Dodge St.
Nebraska

BISMARCK, N. DAK. 58501—420 N. Fourth St.
North Dakota, South Dakota

DENVER, COLO. 80215—1401 Saulsbury
Colorado, Utah, Wyoming

HELENA, MONTANA 59601—Power Block
Idaho, Montana

PACIFIC COAST DIVISION

BERKELEY, CALIF. 94710—810 University Ave.
Alaska, Arizona, California, Hawaii, Nevada,
Oregon, Washington

LOS ANGELES, CALIF. 90017—1709 W. 8th St.
Southern California

SACRAMENTO, CALIF. 95814—Forum Bldg.
Central and Northern California, Nevada

PHOENIX, ARIZ, 85016—3625 N. 16th St.
Arizona

PORTLAND, ORE. 97225—4475 S.W. Scholls Ferry Rd.

OLYMPIA, WASH. 98502—120 Union Avenue Building
Alaska, Washington

   Printed in U.S.A.

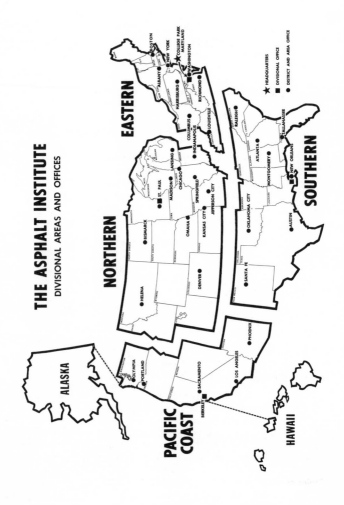

THE ASPHALT INSTITUTE
DIVISIONAL AREAS AND OFFICES

★ HEADQUARTERS
■ DIVISIONAL OFFICE
● DISTRICT AND AREA OFFICE

NORTHERN

EASTERN

SOUTHERN

PACIFIC COAST

ALASKA

HAWAII

BISMARCK

HELENA

DENVER

SANTA FE

OMAHA

KANSAS CITY

JEFFERSON CITY

ST. PAUL

MADISON

CHICAGO

SPRINGFIELD

LANSING

INDIANAPOLIS

COLUMBUS

LOUISVILLE

OKLAHOMA CITY

AUSTIN

PHOENIX

LOS ANGELES

SACRAMENTO

BERKELEY

PORTLAND

OLYMPIA

ALBANY

HARRISBURG

BOSTON

NEW YORK

COLLEGE PARK
MARYLAND

WASHINGTON

RICHMOND

RALEIGH

TALLAHASSEE

ATLANTA

MONTGOMERY

NEW ORLEANS

SOME IMPORTANT TECHNICAL
PUBLICATIONS OF THE ASPHALT INSTITUTE

May 1964

Specification Series

Specifications and Construction Methods for Asphalt Concrete and Other Hot-Mix Types (SS-1)

Specifications for Asphalt Cements and Liquid Asphalt (SS-2)

Specifications and Construction Methods for Asphalt Curbs and Gutters (SS-3)

Asphalt Protective Coatings for Pipe Lines (CS-96)

Manual Series

Thickness Design—Asphalt Pavement Structures for Highways and Streets (MS-1)

Mix Design Methods for Asphalt Concrete and other Hot-Mix Types (MS-2)

Asphalt Plant Manual (MS-3)

The Asphalt Handbook (MS-4)

Introduction to Asphalt (MS-5), (Chapters I-IV of the Asphalt Handbook)

Asphalt Pocketbook of Useful Information (MS-6), (Chapter XV of the Asphalt Handbook)

Asphalt Mulch Treatment (MS-7)

Asphalt Paving Manual (MS-8)

Asphalt for Off-Street Paving and Play Areas (MS-9)

Soil Manual for Design of Asphalt Pavement Structures (MS-10)

Asphalt Pavements for Airports (MS-11)

Asphalt in Hydraulic Structures (MS-12)

Asphalt Surface Treatments and Asphalt Penetration Macadam (MS-13)

Copies of these and other Asphalt Institute publications are available at any Institute field engineering office listed in the end papers, or at Institute Headquarters office at College Park, Maryland

● NOTES ●

<u>LIQUID LIMIT</u>. — POINT WHERE A
SOIL LOSES WATER, TO CEASE TO
BEHAVE LIKE A LIQUID
THE MOISTURE CONTENT AT THIS
STAGE IS THE LIQUID LIMIT.

<u>PLASTIC LIMIT</u>

WHEN ADDITIONAL MOISTURE IS
REMOVED, THE PLASTIC STATE TERMINATES,
THE MOISTURE CONTENT AT THAT
STAGE IS THE PLASTIC LIMIT.

<u>SHRINKAGE LIMIT</u>

WHEN VOLUME CHANGE CEASES
WITH DECREASE IN MOISTURE.

<u>PLASTICITY INDEX</u>

DIFF. BETWEEN LIQUID & PLASTIC
LIMITS

<u>L I</u>   INCREASE WITH INCREASE IN CLAY
OR ORGANIC MATTER

<u>LL</u>   "   "   "   " INORGANIC SOILS